Not Always on the Level

2

E. J. Moran Campbell

E J MORAN CAMPBELL

Not Always on the Level

ISBN 0 7279 0184 2

Printed in Great Britain at the University Press, Cambridge

For Diana

Contents

Introduction

I began writing these reminiscences in 1975 when, after spending seven years in Canada, I returned to England for a sabbatical. Visiting the places where I grew up, had been at medical school, had worked as a junior hospital doctor, and where I had started to do research, and reminiscing with old friends produced an intense awareness of what things had been like. Furthermore I realised that this time had been brief, was over, and was likely to go unrecorded. Country general practice is no longer what it was for my father. The life of a London medical student is not as it was at the end of the war. The lives of a junior doctor and of a struggling clinical scientist are also changed. The urge to tell something of my father was given further impetus by James Herriot's stories about the life of a Yorkshire vet, which brought back the walls, the gorse, the peewits, and the accents of the Dales. So, in an idle moment, I wrote *Seven farm gates*. I enjoyed the experience and went on to write the other stories as and when the exploration of a memory, mood, and time were in harmony. The stories were not, therefore, written in chronological order but I have arranged them to form a sort of patchwork autobiography.

I am a manic depressive. Signs of this condition seem to have been apparent as early as age twenty (*On being a manic depressive*). In retrospect, the state was manifest by about age forty (*Where's McMaster?*) and by the time I was fifty five had become florid (*Bloody bath*; *Highnights*). For most of the time I have been writing these reminiscences I regarded the disorder as just a nuisance but latterly I decided to make use of adversity and have tried to convey what living with a roller coaster mind is like.

Are the stories true? I think so. A few of the episodes have been "assembled" but none is invented and the descriptions of the major characters are as accurate as my memory permits. I cannot, of course, verify the dialogue but I believe it to be as true to the characters as any talk attributed to cricketers by Neville Cardus ("cardusian truth"?).

I have endeavoured to give an impression of the romance and the earthiness of it all. I do not apologise for trying to convey the fun of science and of medicine. Indeed from the usual literary accounts of the creative agonies suffered by writers and painters I suspect science often is more fun – certainly it seems to be much funnier.

I have avoided jargon as far as I can and explained it when I cannot without, I hope, spoiling the flow. Names, however, have been a problem. Sometimes I mention published research, which means that the names of the authors are on record; elsewhere I describe episodes involving people, particularly patients, who might not like to see their names in print. Although the distinction between these suggests that some simple rule might be observed, no rule is easy to apply in practice and so I have used my judgement. I apologise both to those who appear and do not wish to, and vice versa.

As can be imagined, the raw material of this book was a mess. Janet Burke prevented me from leaving it in a drawer. She sorted out, prepared many drafts, and kept me going. I also thank Stephen Lock and Norma Pearce for improving it.

The narrative

Our branch of the Clan Campbell was originally from Argyll but had settled many generations previously in Perthshire, which is properly in the realm of the Breadalbane Campbells. My father said the founder of the branch had originally been the Catholic tutor to the daughters of the Duke of Argyll and had run off with one of his charges at the time of the Reformation and changed his cloth.

THE CAMPBELLS, MORANS, AND O'CALLAGHANS

My father was Edward Gordon Campbell, born 1886, the son of Edward Campbell of George's Park, Tipperary in Ireland who, in turn, was the son of James Campbell of Blairgowrie near Coupar Angus in Perthshire.

James Campbell was a landowner of some substance who had seven sons and two daughters (in that order) and my grandfather was the sixth of the seven sons. He had a classical education at Edinburgh University and it was then intended that he should go and seek his fortune in the Argentine. There was, however, a revolution in that country and my grandfather got no further than Ireland where he eventually became the estate manager for the Duke of Leinster. He was a Presbyterian but married my grandmother, Ellen Moran, who came from a long line of Episcopalians. She converted him. The Morans were supposed to be descended from Dermot McMurragh, the king of Munster, but their more recent claim to fame was Lord Gifford, a cousin of my grandmother's, who was one of the leading legal figures in London in the nineteenth century.

My father was the second son and the third child in a family of four. Little is known about his elder sister May but his elder brother Kenneth went to South Africa and died in Ladysmith. His younger brother, after suffering shell shock in the First World War, settled into the family home at George's Park. My father went to Trinity College, Dublin and put himself through an arts degree by working as a schoolmaster in England before studying divinity and being ordained in the Church of Ireland (ie the Episcopal church) in 1911. He served as a padre in France from 1914 to 1917 (see *Amateur anaesthetist*), after which he studied medicine (see *The troubles with midwifery*) and became Medical Officer to the engineering firm building the reservoir at Scar Village in Yorkshire for the Bradford Corporation Waterworks. He married my mother in 1922. I was born in Scar Village in 1925, and my brother Brian in 1928.

In 1928 my father moved down the valley to Ripley and started a general practice. He moved into Harrogate and also acquired a practice in Birstwith in 1931. He built these up very rapidly and took on an assistant and then a junior partner, so that by 1938 he had a very large practice. There is little doubt that this success was well merited: my father was far ahead of his time both in the medicine he practised and in the standard of service he provided. It was said in the dale, "by the time you've got back from the village telephone, Dr Campbell is already at the farm".

In 1943, at the age of fifty seven, my father had a myocardial infarction after which he did not work as hard. In 1952 he developed carcinoma of the prostate, which killed him unpleasantly in 1959.

My mother was Clare Irene O'Callaghan, daughter of James O'Callaghan, the rector of Rathvilly, Kildare. She said that the O'Callaghans had come to Ireland with Cromwell – but the name does not support this story. My father met her when she was a young schoolgirl and they married when she was twenty four or twenty five. My mother had no particular education or occupation that I know of before she married. She died of a stroke in 1964.

I was educated at Clifton House School, a private preparatory school in Harrogate; at Wedderburn, a private post-preparatory tutorial establishment attached to Clifton House; at King James' Grammar School in Knaresborough; and at the Harrogate Technical College night school. After working as a pathology technician, I went to the Middlesex Hospital Medical School in London in 1943; did a BSc with Samson Wright in 1946; and graduated in 1949. After house jobs at the Middlesex and Brompton Hospitals, during which I acquired the MD and the MRCP, I became lecturer in physiology at the Middlesex Hospital Medical School, where I also acquired a PhD. My thesis was on *The muscular control of breathing in man*, which formed the basis of a small monograph *The respiratory muscles and the mechanics of breathing* (published in 1958).

Between 1953 and 1954 I was registrar at the Middlesex Hospital and after that was Comyns-Berkeley Fellow of the Middlesex Hospital and Gonville and Caius College, Cambridge, which I held at the Johns Hopkins Hospital in Baltimore, Maryland. This completed my training in respiratory physiology and medicine. In 1955 I was appointed "assistant" (ie assistant professor) to the professor of medicine at the Middlesex Hospital Medical School. In 1962, I was appointed lecturer, and later senior lecturer, at the Postgraduate Medical School (later the Royal Postgraduate Medical School) and physician to the Hammersmith Hospital. In 1968, I became RS McLaughlin professor and chairman of the Department of Medicine at McMaster University in Hamilton, Ontario – a post I held until 1975.

I married Diana Mary Elisabeth Green, daughter of Ernest and Hilda Green of Writtle, Chelmsford, Essex in 1954. Ernest Green was trained by Rutherford in Manchester and was an engineer at Marconi's. Diana was a nurse at the Middlesex Hospital. We have four children – Fiona, Susan, Robert, and Jessica.

I have written several books and a number of papers,

mostly on basic and applied respiratory physiology. I suppose I am chiefly associated with three contributions: the first comprehensive study of the respiratory muscles; the controlled oxygen method for treating respiratory failure; and a popular but inadequate theory of the mechanism of the sensation of breathlessness. More broadly I am interested in the way scientists and doctors solve problems and how to help rather than hinder students in the acquisition of these mental habits.

An amateur anaesthetist on the Western Front

My father was a parson who became a doctor because of the Great War. His mother came from a staunch, Episcopalian, southern Irish family and wanted one of her sons to do well in the church because many generations of the Morans since Cromwell had produced a bishop. My father was the middle son and he was the only one who tried to fulfil his mother's wishes.

He grew up in Tipperary, went to school in Kilkenny, and then put himself through Dublin University – Trinity College Dublin or TCD as it was variously known and still is – by working as a schoolmaster first on the Scottish borders and later in Kent. He gained a BA from TCD, having spent only a year or so actually in residence. In 1911, after a year studying divinity, he was ordained a priest of the Church of Ireland. The established Church of Ireland is Anglican and Episcopalian, though of course over 90% of the southern Irish are what Spike Milligan calls "catlicks" or what Orangemen call "Papishes".

For the next three years Father followed the usual career of a young cleric, spending a few months here and there as a junior curate. In 1913 he was appointed curate to the rector of Rathvilly just across the border of Carlow, on the southern side of the Wicklow mountains, about forty miles from Dublin. The landowners, large farmers, and other professional, middle class folk made up his flock.

In some ways the social and religious set up was like Quebec: Dublin with TCD was like Montreal with McGill. There was one big difference, however, everybody, whatever

Published in part in the *British Medical Journal*, 1979; ii: 1667–70.

his religion, spoke English in the home counties around Dublin. Erse, the Irish form of Gaelic, was then, as it is now, common only in the far west. Without the badge of language it was sometimes difficult to distinguish a middle class Catholic from a middle class Protestant. Accent might help but, as my Episcopalian mother would say, "some Catholics are quite well spoken", using the same tone of voice as one would to say, "some of my best friends are...".

When middle class Irish or their offspring meet on neutral ground there commonly ensues a subtle probing of "what school? what university? who do you work for?" which is used to get to the heart of the matter of "where do you and I stand in the age old relationship?". If the answer to the question about university is "National" (University College, Dublin otherwise known as UCD), then the declaration is "I am a Catholic, even if I am an atheist". If the answer is TCD, then the declaration is "I am probably of lukewarm religious persuasion, but culturally a Protestant". I think the reason many Trinity men don the Trinity tie every day of their lives is to avoid these probings. After all, might as well let the other chap know you are from the master race at the outset of any cocktail party conversation!

There were snags about these guidelines. Some of the Catholic upper crust preferred their children to go to TCD. A special dispensation from the church used to be needed but with the passage of time it was often not sought and nothing was said.

In secure, fox hunting, squireen Rathvilly my father fell in love with the rector's daughter. And in August 1914, aged about sixteen, she became the girl he left behind him as the Dublin Fusiliers' regimental song foretold of many an Irishman who went off to the wars.

As soon as the war broke out my father sought permission to be a soldier. There were none more loyal to King and country than the Anglo-Irish who, throughout history, have supplied some of the best generals, from Wellington to Alanbrooke, Alexander and Montgomery. They were like the officer class in the southern United States in this regard. The bishop flatly refused, however, on what I take to be sound clerical grounds, so my father became a padre, as chaplains used to be called, on the Western Front. As the family name was Campbell he was posted to the Argyll and Sutherland Highlanders. Officially that was a sensible decision but in practice it put him in an awkward position. Almost all of the men were Presbyterians and many did not have "the English" as their natural tongue. His care of souls was largely restricted to the officers, who were not exactly delighted to have an Irish padre in their Highland mess.

My father's war, like that of so many others, was a bore punctuated by the dangers, disasters, and horrors of trench warfare. When the Western Front was active he was well within the range of German guns, ministering to the wounded and the dying in a casualty clearing station just behind the lines.

For a time he was in the same unit as Arthur Martin-Leake, RAMC, who was the first man ever to win a bar to the Victoria Cross. In fact for a while he was at risk of being the only man ever to be awarded the VC twice, because such was his modesty that his commanding officer did not know that he had already picked up one in the Boer War. One of the only other two men to win the VC and bar was also an officer in the Royal Army Medical Corps – a doctor's life in wartime can be dangerous.

According to my father, Martin-Leake was diffident and painfully shy. He was second in rank in the casualty clearing station and was always discomfited when left in charge. He would only speak about the exploits that earned him the VC with embarrassment. "I just had to help the poor chaps. I suppose I knew there were bullets and shrapnel flying about but I honestly didn't think about them."

When the casualties were pouring in at the Battle of the Somme my father volunteered to help keep a patient anaesthetised, thus allowing one doctor to serve as anaesthetist to two doctors doing the surgery. There were no professional anaesthetists, just one of the medical officers who dropped ether or chloroform on a rag mask clapped over the patient's nose and mouth. To begin with the anaesthetist would "put the patient under" and leave my father to "keep him down".

My father, however, became quite expert and after a time was fully accepted as a proper anaesthetist when the load of casualties was more than the regular staff could cope with. I keep expecting something similar to happen in M*A*S*H – the possible combinations of heroism and humour seem irresistible. Undoubtedly my father felt more worthwhile giving anaesthetics to those who might live than administering the last rites to those who would not.

For a while he was attached to the Canadians at Vimy Ridge. In 1954, without telling him, I deviated from the direct holiday route home from Paris to Calais to visit some places he had mentioned when reminiscing about the war. We stopped at the Canadian memorial at Vimy Ridge. There in the drizzle we separated for a few minutes. I ambled over the dreary terrain thinking of Robert Graves and *Goodbye to All That* then came quietly back to find him mopping a face that was streaming with tears. He mumbled, "Magnificent troops. Damn fools. Coming all those thousands of miles to be sent walking to death by those bloody fools of generals at HQ. Lions they were, led by donkeys."

Having served three and a half years in France, my father was posted back to Dublin where he was seconded to the bishop as a general purpose locum tenens who would fill in for any church that needed a parson at the weekend. There were plenty of these churches because the Protestant clergy had all joined up. He was based in Dublin and would go off wherever he was needed on his motorbike on Saturday or Sunday. The rest of the week was his own.

By this time he was having spiritual scruples. He remained a mild Christian throughout his life and occasionally officiated in the local churches. His sonorous reading of the lessons and his big frame in full clerical garb made my mother burst with pride; and I was also proud of the medals on his chest. But, as he put it to me when I was in my teens, "It is difficult to resolve one's doubts when one is paid to persuade others to suspend theirs."

He decided to try and get a more useful degree than his BA, perhaps in science, and then go back to teaching and went to see the Registrar at Trinity College. The registrar, hearing of his experiences in the casualty clearing station, dropped the hint that there was a vacant place in the medical school. Father always asserted that this was the first time the possibility of becoming a doctor had ever occurred to him. He told me he went out and walked around the grounds of Trinity for an hour thinking about where he would get the money to support himself (now aged thirty one) for another four years at university; what the attitude of the bishop would be; how it would mean postponing marriage to my mother; and so on. He decided. That was Friday, on Tuesday he started in medical school. Trinity asked no questions and the bishop was prepared to turn a blind eye – just as long as Father and his motorbike were available at weekends (he only occasionally called for father's services during the week).

Some of the weekend assignments were as hazardous as the casualty clearing station because these were the times of the "Troubles" in southern Ireland. A lone motorcyclist inevitably attracted attention. He did not think he was ever shot at but he was often stopped by a tree across the road or a nondescript brandishing a gun. My father became a dab hand at these ambushes. He would stop the engine of his bike and sit still to indicate to those in ambush that he was not going to make a run for it. He would take off his goggles and tweed cap (worn back to front, of course) to show his bald head and would unwrap his scarf to reveal the dog collar which, by now, he wore only when on church business. Then he waited for someone to come out from hiding, cover him with a second gun, and start questioning.

Both regular and "irregular" troops used these roadblocks but they were generally manned by the local police ("polis", in my mother's tongue) or by the Royal Irish Constabulary. Most to be feared were the rebels, the Sinn Feiners. Sometimes the posse might be composed of vigilantes trying to protect their homes. Then there were the British Army and the Black and Tans, who were so named after their peculiar uniform, a mixture of black jackets and khaki trousers or vice versa. The accent of the questioner might settle the issue. To my father a respectful upper class accent, whether Irish or English, was reassuring but a more natural Irish accent could mean either the rebels or the cops. An English accent was not necessarily reassuring. If lower class, it might mean regular army or the hated Black and Tans, a militia Lloyd George had hastily scoured – if my mother was to be believed – from the scum of the English gaols. To the Black and Tans, all Irish were the same "just bloody wogs".

The opening questions, in addition to the betrayal by accent, established my father's ostensible business but sometimes were not of themselves a sufficient alibi. To support his bona fide Father always strapped a single, small Gladstone bag on the carrier behind him which contained his clerical garb and silver comunion set. The Royal Irish Constabulary and the British regulars were usually satisfied by now and would let him go, often with a hint about where to be careful further down the road. The other groups, however, remained suspicious and would try to establish where his loyalities lay with some question such as "Who are you for?". This is a shortened form of the challenge "Are you a Billy or a Dan, or an old tin can?". Father, with a nod at the gun, would reply, "I think I'd be wiser to keep my mouth shut until I know who you're for." If the group was Irish the matter usually ended there and Father went on his way. He was only really in danger once when a drunken Black and Tan was all for shooting him out of hand in reprisal for a rebel attack the night before. Fortunately the group was under the command of a Glaswegian ex-corporal still wearing the badge of the Highland Light Infantry. When my father asked him where he had served and they had shared talk of the war in France, the corporal made it clear that the Black and Tan would be shot before my father was.

So the years passed. My father worked his way through medical school; he continued to woo my mother in a desultory way; and the Troubles in Ireland quietened down, only to flare up again in 1922.

Troubles with midwifery

By the summer of 1921 my father was in difficulties. The bishop had let him stay nearly three years in the cushy job of relief man for the parishes around Dublin, thus requiring him to be a parson only at weekends. The bishop, however, needed the post for bright young clerics waiting for good livings and there was something rather deceitful about my father's use of the job to retread himself as a doctor. In any case the final year or so of medical school, with its work in hospital and more frequent and rigorous exams, made it difficult for Pa to meet even the small call the Church made on his time. He had continued to drift towards marriage, uncertain I suspect how much the prompting came from love and how much from honour or inability to face the shame of breaking off the relationship not only with Mother but with the whole family. After all James O'C, though the incumbent of a minor living, was a respected and scholarly member of the Dublin bishopric – and I suspect Pa borrowed from him to finish medical school.

My father decided to try and qualify early. The odd timing of his entry to medical school in 1918 meant that he had a head start on those in the class of 1922 in which the regulations of the university placed him. He was pretty sure he could pass finals in 1921 but discreet enquiries made it fairly clear that he would not be permitted to sit them. In any case the closing date for entry was past so that permission could come only from the senior administration of the school. He did not want to disturb them because they, like the bishop,

Published in part in the *British Medical Journal*, 1979; ii: 1667–70.

were also having to turn the odd blind eye to this part time medical student.

He stumbled on a ruse. There were examinations in the autumn for those who failed in the summer, and at the last possible moment Pa put in an application to sit these, trusting that it would be processed at a junior level and evade the registrar's attention. The ruse worked and Pa passed. In fact, he did very well in several subjects including coming top in medical jurisprudence, a subject he had not yet been taught!

Of course the facts came to light and the registrar said Pa really could not be allowed to get away with it. Technically the registrar could have ruled the examination results invalid. (Had he done so and had Pa failed a year later it would have been a wry comment on the validity of exams, which they often deserve.) The registrar ruled, however, that Pa need not take the exams again but that his degree would be withheld until the proper time – nearly a year later.

Without his degree Pa was not qualified. He need not study very seriously but the registrar hinted that his ruling would be more acceptable to the senior professors if Pa made at least some show of attendance. The problem of earning a living, however, was not solved. By now neither the bishop's nor Pa's consciences could allow him to continue as a cleric; so what was he to do?

I'm afraid I don't know exactly how the time was spent but he certainly packed two things into the next year or so, each of which should normally have taken a year.

Firstly, less germane to this story and in any case without pay, he took the Diploma in Public Health. He later made some use of this as a part time rural medical officer of health in Upper Nidderdale. It seemed to him to be an insurance against the difficulty he anticipated as an ex-parson in obtaining employment in private or other clinical practice.

Secondly he became houseman at the Rotunda, at that time probably the best known "Lying-in" hospital in Britain. Although unpaid, this at least gave him food and lodging. After a brief period working in the hospital he was put in charge of "the district". I know pretty well what this entailed because twenty five years later I spent a memorable month on the district at the Rotunda myself and afterwards we compared our experiences. We found we had certainly worked in the same streets, possibly even the same houses. It is not beyond Irish possibility that we attended the same women!

What set him aside from all the other postgraduates at that time was the right to "put on forceps". These are like an outsize pair of sugar tongs which come apart at the hinge. Each forceps is passed into the mother's vagina on either side of the infant's head; the two halves are then coupled together and used to draw the baby out. This sounds all very well in principle, but in practice the use of forceps could be dicey. This was particularly so in an obstructed labour where the pelvic outlet was small, the baby big, or something had got in the way. On these occasions too much "heave-ho" could make matters worse for all parties; and there was no ambulance to whisk mother away for a caesarean section.

My father would reminisce with relish about the first time out in the district he put on the forceps. He was being watched by an Indian postgraduate and two students. In fact his experience in the hospital had been limited, as he was usually co-pilot to one of the senior staff rather than a solo operator. Pa slowly and deliberately described what he was going to do step by step for his own sake, leaving the others to take his muttering as "teaching". All went very smooothly and afterwards the Indian, who was, of course, nearly 10 years younger than my father and did not know his background, said in an accent that I imagine anticipated Peter Sellers, "My goodness, Sir, that was damnably skilful! How many dozens have you done?" My father claims that he replied offhandedly that he supposed he had done four or five!

One evening some months later, Pa and two students were preparing to deliver a baby in a bedroom of a decaying Georgian house about a mile from the hospital when they heard Crossley tenders drive in and pull up at each end of the street. A Crossley tender was a small truck with soldiers, guns at the ready, in the back and covered by netting to ward off missiles. These vehicles were unpopular with the troops because the netting seemed – indeed was – a flimsy protection and they were unpopular with the populace because the troops were understandably trigger happy. The sounds that followed the arrival of the tenders, the banging on doors and rough speech, bespoke a house to house search.

The door of the room opened and a frightened young man entered. He hesitated because preparations for delivery had not yet been made so it was not obvious what was going on. A hubbub downstairs indicated that the search was closing in.

"Get under there" said my father, nodding to the bed with its ample coverings.

"Keep your mouths shut!" he told students and hurriedly put the woman in the delivery position and donned his gown and mask.

After a few minutes the door opened again and a young officer of the regular army entered, immediately recognised the midwifeliness of what was going on, but began: "I beg your pardon, Sir, but have you seen..."

Father cut him off with a gesture of his hands indicating that his question was absurd, thereby avoiding the lie direct.

"I'm very sorry" said the courteous young oppressor of the Irish race and left.

When the sounds of the search had receded and the Crossleys had driven away, Pa prodded the body under the bed with his foot using more than the requisite force.

"Get out of here, you damn young fool!"

The lad left, saying nothing. A few weeks later, on a tram, Pa was vaguely aware of a young man watching him across the aisle. Just before a stop the man got up, came over, and said, "Sir, I didn't think to thank you the other night. I should have."

Pa did not recognise him but could only think he was the would-be Hero of the Irish Revolution who had hidden under the bed.

Nidderdalefolk

Father was offered a position as assistant master at the Rotunda, but could not afford to take it and tried to find a job as an assistant in general practice in England. He was unsuccessful and pointed out the prejudice which he thought was responsible. Imagine his *curriculum vitae* in 1923.

Born 1886 (that is, now thirty seven);

Qualified 1922;

Previous occupation: cleric/parson/priest.

No general practitioner was keen to employ a middle aged former parson with very little experience.

Eventually he found a job as resident medical officer in the village – Scar Village – built to house the navvies employed by Bradford Corporation to build their dam (for water for the city, not hydro) at the head of Nidderdale.

Nidderdale is the least known of the major dales, probably because it is "blind" and there is no way out of the head of it. The range of Whernside cuts it off from Wharfedale, which curls up from the southwest and abuts Wensleydale on the north. There are roads connecting these two dales with Nidderdale at Pateley Bridge but they have formidable hills ("banks") and are ten miles south of the head of the dale. Close to the head of the dale the historic old Drovers' Road crossed from north to south but this is now covered by the reservoir. It can still be walked but even in the twenties it was steep and rough enough to be used in an international, six day, motorcycle trial – one of my earliest memories. The road takes its name from the route by which sheep were driven down from the Scottish borders to the woollen mills in the West Riding before the advent of Australian wool.

Scar Village was a small "company town" built to last

three to five years and accommodate the engineers, navvies, and others building the dam. Actually it is the second Bradford Corporation Waterworks dam in the dale. About four miles further up there is another older one whose name I think is Angram. The works were connected to the outside world, the little town of Pateley Bridge, by a twisty, narrow road and by the Nidd Valley Light Railway. At Pateley the dale is almost a mile wide and the bottom is sufficiently fertile to support mixed farming but the hills rise steeply on either side to gorse and heather covered uplands able to support only a few sheep.

The valley twists and narrows above Pateley, passing through various thwaites (Norse for "clearing" or "paddock") to Lofthouse (Norse again), a fair sized and prosperous village, but above this becomes almost a defile. The older farmers up there still remembered my father even as recently as the 'fifties. They had strange Nordic names and spoke an almost incomprehensible dialect. It was not just a Yorkshire accent. The speech was full of relics of Norse and the second person singular ("thee", pronounced "thah") was standard.

"Gi ower laikin, tha mun oppen t'geeut" Translation: stop playing and get the gate open.

"Wilt' awa coop?" Translation: Will thou have a cup?

"Ee's nobbut 'armless." Translation: He is nothing but harmless – he means no harm; is just stupid.

Father had a small "sick bay" with three or four beds looked after by a state registered nurse. The nearest hospital was at Harrogate, thirty miles and two hours away, and in 1923 that hospital was no big deal. Thus my father was the "health care system" and obviously thoroughly enjoyed himself. There was plenty of trauma from "the works" and plenty of midwifery from the Irish navvy wives. Socially, there was companionship from the resident managers and engineers. He read. He walked over the hills picking out the wildflowers and listening to the peewits and curlews. He had a wife, a small bungalow, and a motorbike. He also had an income.

When his services were no longer required at the dam,

Father moved down the dale and set up in practice – "hung up his shingle" – in Ripley.

We lived in Ripley from 1928 to 1931, in a large house which was cheap because it was also in very poor repair. You meet it on the right, a four square, stone place with slate roof, as you enter the village from the southern roundabout, which was, thankfully, built before the war and helped to save the physical character of the little town. Opposite hides the vicarage, which, as I remember it, was a yellow stucco building but so shrouded in trees that my mind's eye cannot see the whole outside of the house, even having been there so many times. Round the gentle curve comes the church with marks on the walls said to have been made by bullets from Cromwell's men during the mopping up operations after the Battle of Marston Moor (1644). After the church is the market place with its cobbles and stocks. There hasn't been a regular market in Ripley, as far as I know, for centuries but it is solid evidence that it was once a town, and unless somebody else has been imprisoned in the stocks, the last was my younger brother whom I once pelted with tomatoes. Indeed Ripley can still claim to be a town because the town charter received from Elizabeth I has never been revoked. Some said it was the smallest town in England, properly speaking: or so Father told me but he was not sufficiently interested to pursue the matter.

The character of Ripley is feudal and in the late 'twenties it still behaved in a feudal manner. Ripley had been bypassed by time and had stayed small enough not only to be owned by the baronets Ingilby but governed by them. I do not remember the baronet: Father said he was not a bad chap and was a good enough landlord but his father and grandfather before him had "held Ripley back" by refusing to have the railway. The real force in Father's day was Lady Ingilby. I remember her as a large person resembling an outsize Queen Mary (the person, not the ship) in dress and deportment. She used to carry on "as though she owned the place", which by rights she did, but even in the twenties it was a bit much that she had denied Ripley a pub, wouldn't tolerate gossiping at open front doors, received a hint of a curtsey from all the women, and had to be forced to allow a post office and a bus stop in the town. Still, it's an ill wind...because the Ingilby's welcomed the bypass on the road from Harrogate to Ripon and the north side of Nidderdale.

The Ingilbys live in Ripley Castle. As boys we were occasionally allowed into the grounds to skate on the lake or take part in jubilee or coronation pageants on the lawns but the castle itself was not open to the public. Times change, however, and on a recent visit I found that it was laying open its charms like many another stately home. Indeed it is so photogenic that it has appeared in several films and television programmes.

Father did not fit in with the establishment in Ripley. He was Irish, of uncertain class, and an ex-clergyman to boot, which made him non grata to the firmly Church of England Ingilbys and their appointees in the diocese.

I remember only one direct encounter between Lady I and my father, several years after we had moved to Harrogate but while most of the village was still on Father's panel. He got out of the car in the market place and hailed her politely but firmly. "Lady I, I want a word with you." Having done that he avoided any further direct form of address and certainly would never have called her "Milady". As he approached her he wiped the drip he always carried on the end of his nose when he was excited, using the large brown silk Paisley hanky drawn from his sleeve.

The conversation opened with bland pleasantries but then came a warning sign. He pushed his bifocals up to his forehead and extended his neck in an affectation of supporting them. He did this whenever seeking to dominate someone of comparable stature. He stood six feet and was still built like the powerful centre threequarter who had played at centre and at wing forward in the Border League.

Facing Lady I at short range, the spectacle raising ploy was essential if he was going to shoot down his nose at her because inch for inch and pound for pound, she was nearly his match.

"Will you mind not phoning my wife to ask about one of my patients?"

"I suppose you mean Ethel Hardcastle?"

"I do. If you want to know anything about Ethel, you should ask me and I'll tell you what I think you should know."

"But they're our tenants and Ethel was our scullery maid."

"Well why not ask me?"

"Because I know you won't tell me."

"Exactly. Ethel may have been your maid and may be your tenant but she's my patient and the times have gone when she and her like were your chattels."

"But I meant no harm."

"You never do. Good day to you."

And he turned away, not rudely but firmly enough to show who had given audience to whom. She, not wishing to lose more face by speaking to his departing shoulder, turned a second later.

Ripley's ambitions, if it ever had any were frustrated during the Middle Ages and later up until the early nineteenth century by its proximity to Ripon in the north and Knaresborough to the south east. Since then it has been overshadowed by the upstart Harrogate with its spa and the nouveaux riches commuting to Leeds and Bradford.

Ripon, with its bishopric, cathedral, and market, is seven or eight miles away on the Ure, the only river not to give its name to its dale, which takes its name from the village of Wensley. Upper Wensleydale in Father's time was the practice of a man who was to become the most famous general practitioner of his time – William Pickles. I think I once met Dr Pickles when I was very young, out walking with my father on the moors above Douthwaite Reservoir. His few clinical contacts with Pickles had won Father's respect but their contacts were few. Father had left Ramsgill and Lofthouse at the top of Nidderdale before Pickles established himself in Aysgarth. The top of the dale was the practice of Charles Flintoff, our beloved Uncoman (Uncle Man), who delivered us. He was my father's advisor, closest friend, and patient until he died of a stroke in the early 'fifties. Uncoman lived in Pateley Bridge. Father used to "cover" for Uncoman during his rare holidays or illnesses, so occasionally Father's rounds took him as far up the dale as Lofthouse. Even Uncoman had little contact with Pickles, however, because the roads between Upper Nidderdale and the lower part of Wensleydale were poor, the hills unpopulated, and so their practices scarcely touched.

I think Father would have been a match for Pickles as an epidemiologist because his note keeping was impeccable. As he left each house, whenever I was in the car, he would make an economical three line note about the patient he had just seen so that there was never any problem should one of his assistants have to take over from him. I can, however, only remember him once coming near to writing a medical article. It was during one of the polio epidemics of the mid-thirties, when he was an enthusiast for sulphonamides. He always called them "M & B", although in fact he wrote specifically on his prescription pad "sulpha whatever, not May and Bakers". "Bad for the family to think I give M & B for everything", he said in regard to the initials stamped on the pills.

The event in my mind was probably really provoked by an accident of diagnosis rather than an obedience to any experimental design. He gave sulphonamides to one of two identical twins who slept in the same bed, went to the same school, and developed upper respiratory tract infections at the same time. I think he only gave sulphonamide to one because she had a history of middle ear infections and "might have been incubating a mastoid." The twin not on the drug developed crippling paralysis; the one taking sulphonamide had none.

"Sinclair Miller" (the local clinical pathologist, an MRCP, and a man of some eminence in the town), "wanted me to write it up. Didn't have the time. Would have made an ass of myself if I had," he told me many years later, post-Salk.

Father knew the head of Nidderdale well from the years he had spent at Scar Village and we still had the privilege of a key that unlocked the gate at the foot of the hill leading up to Middlesmoor, and would drive up the splendid canyon with a view of Scar Dam as one rounded a final corner to the left.

Knaresborough is five or six miles south east of Ripley through the village of Nidd, from which I imagine the river and dale take their name. I suppose it could be t'otherway round because Nidd is a small straggling place without any evidence of a heart of a history such as Ripley wears on her sleeve.

Knaresborough is very old, thriving, and one of the loveliest towns in Yorkshire. The houses are steeply stacked round a bend in the river with a handsome railway bridge. Knaresborough has a market place, a bishop (but no cathedral), an old castle where the murderers of Thomas Becket went to ground, a witch's cave (Mother Shipton's), the Dropping Well with its stalactites and all manner of petrified artefacts, and an excellent grammar school named after James I, or as Father used to say "Really, James VI." In 1942, I used to cycle the four mile switchback down from Harrogate to Starbeck, up to the golf course, down to the river bridge, and up and over the High Street in Knaresborough. The return journey in the blackout, up the two long pulls to Starbeck and then past the hospital to the Stray, into a drizzling west wind after a football game sometimes made me wish I had gone to the local Harrogate Grammar School. In my heart and head though, I knew Father was right to pay the extra nine pounds a year for my schooling in Knaresborough rather than where we lived in Harrogate, where it would have been free. Furthermore whatever the regulations about 11 plus entrance examinations, I am sure the headmaster of Harrogate Grammar School would have grabbed me hungrily as a member of the professional class who, in their snobbery, preferred to send their sons to one of the several, very dubious, minor public schools in the area if they couldn't afford to send them to Sedburgh (for the tough), Bootham (for the Quakers and non-conformists), Ambleforth (for the Catlicks), or the up and coming Worksop (for the rugger).

Having no sisters I had no concern with or knowledge of schooling for girls. When puberty arrived my interest was lavished on a very similar girls' preparatory school (preparatory for what?) before I went to the Knaresborough co-educational school. There in addition to girls there were punts on the river in which, provided one was skilful enough to get up the rapids, one could be very cosy under a tarpaulin.

23

There were two very classy girls' private schools in Harrogate to which none of the local girls that I knew went – the Ladies' College, which I believe was good as well as classy, and Queen Ethelburgas (what a good name for a slightly bent, fast food joint), which was just classy. Ethelburgas was "taken over" during the war but afterwards there was a period during which it was in business again while the neighbouring military camp was a US military hospital. I suspect that some of the classy girls had a bit of the stuffing knocked out of them (material there for several puns or "doobler ontonders") in the bracken and gorse below Birk Crag.

Father started medicine too late in life for his originality to find public expression and, in any case, he was a workaholic, a sorcerer's apprentice consumed by the demands of an expanding practice and nagged by financial worries about "what would become of you and your mother if anything happened to me?". After all he was forty when I was born. I know now that these financial worries were, at any rate by the beginning of the war, quite needless but they dominated our lives when growing up. "Do you think I'm made of money?" was his gruff response to a request from Mother for an increase in her allowance to cope with wartime housekeeping or for my brother or myself for a new bicycle.

He latterly once let slip that he grossed ten thousand pounds in the financial year 1938 to 1939. This "boast" emerged in the late 'fifties after a visit to the chief local tax inspector who had had a coronary. He told me that as an expression of his respect the tax man had quizzically asked him, "Do you know how I picked you for my doctor? When I came to Harrogate in 1939 your tax returns were the promptest, most complete, and biggest of all the doctors around. So I thought that is going to be my man if I need a doctor."

I think Father's money worries had several causes. First of all he had had to pay his way through university twice; he had never ceased expanding the practice; and had just taken out a mortgage on a larger house when the war came. During the war he could never get regular or adequate help. His young partner joined up and the supply of assistants from the local hospital junior staff dried up as they were called up. He had a terrible habit, however, of blaming his pretended poverty on my mother. Although Mother was certainly pretentious, had no sense of money, and was lavish in her entertaining she never spent a great deal on herself. She was a sort of Irish-Jewish momma. Ultimately, Father's way with money – to be blunt, his downright meanness – was symptomatic of his depressive personality. Certainly, he was quite a wealthy man when he died. The clue to the fact that his meanness was symptomatic rather than simply an expression of miserliness, however, is to be found in the estate I found after his death. He knew he was dying six months before the event. He had extensive cancer in the pelvis and tubes in both his kidneys. He began to make desultory "final arrangements" with Cabby Driver, our solicitor. "But he never told me the half of it," said Cabby during hurried meetings in the final weeks. "If only he had, I could have used the loopholes in the laws on death duty to save tens of thousands." There was, indeed, a comeuppance, which was visited on us rather than Father after he died and the estate was cleared of duties. One of the small businesses in the town went bankrupt and it turned out that Father had indulged in some sort of bartering, which, though trivial, was bare faced tax evasion. Cabby got us off lightly but, "Had your dad been alive, it would have cost him a pretty penny – not to mention the scandal in a gossipy place like Harrogate."

Cabby was not a local, never liked the town, and had moved to York years before, only retaining long standing clients who were, like Father, also personal friends.

Certainly the one thing I regret and even resent about Father was his tightfisted way with money. My resentment comes not from personal hardship. My brother and I had a very comfortable upbringing, clouded only by the petty jealousies of prissy public school friends who were even more spoiled than us by parents who had "more money than sense" as our poor mother would loyally say. We were also marvellously well fed by the combination of Mother's cunning at the shops and the enormous quantities of food Father brought home from the farms. "In lieu of," he would say as he hid the eggs, ham, or whatever under a blanket among the medical bags in the back of the car. I was certainly brought to earth with a jolt when faced with the reality of living within a ration book in London from 1943 until rationing ended in the early 'fifties.

No, I do not resent Father's meanness for myself but for my mother. She was admittedly extravagant, partly out of natural generosity and partly as a show off to the social climbers of Harrogate, but he gave her an absurdly small allowance for the housekeeping and later, when they parted for a few years, for herself. Mother was not very articulate and was no match for Father who, until I came to write these pieces, always seemed to have the better case. But dinner times were poisoned by his snide remarks and occasional outbursts. Once a month he would roll in from his evening surgery with a few bills in his hand, his heavy cheeks sagging and not a hint of the pleasant wrinkle we hoped for round his eyes. He would throw the bills on Mother's plate, push his spectacles up to his pate, bring out the large hanky, and wipe it all over parts of his visage.

"Damn it, Woman!" (I never heard any endearment to her face in our presence until a few days before he died, and he would only use her name when bellowing for her as he came into the house looking for her because of a problem in the practice or with a car.) The wiping finished, the hanky would be returned to the left sleeve where it was usually kept with a generous corner protruding. Then he would continue. "This can't go on – and on. Do you think I'm made of money?"

Then, having moved to the big chair at the head of the table, with a spread of his huge but strangely gentle hands towards my brother and myself at ninety degrees at either side he would exclaim, "What's to become of these two if they have to depend on you after I'm gone!" In view of their difference in age and the known greater longevity of women, the presumption that he would predecease her was reasonable. Its imminence was not but certainly his hints of mortality had me persistently scared that I would be left without the means of finishing my education.

26

I also resent the meanness I acquired from Father, although how much by inheritance and how much by habit I cannot tell. I stinted myself as a student and find it difficult to get the balance right in my present role of parent. I think I am right not to have swung the other way and gone along with the preposterous, conspicuously consumptive affluence of many of the children I meet but I am nagged by the fear that I may be wrong and should try to avoid the Scroogiform habits of my father. Occasional bouts of absurd generosity only puzzle the children and do not do the trick.

Although, as far as I know, my father had no firm political allegiance, unlike most of the doctors in Harrogate he welcomed the National Health Service. His income certainly improved but I think he was chiefly relieved to be rid of the old panel system which did not cover families. We received several bits of furniture and other gifts in the wills of people who had not been able to pay their bills. These gifts did not please Pa, "I know they can't pay their bills but money shouldn't enter into medicine." Naive but admirable.

Seven farm gates and one blue man

Going on his rounds with my father started as far back as I remember and was a part of my life to some extent until he died when I was in my mid-'thirties. As a youngster it was almost an undiluted pleasure to go out in the car and play in the farms while he made his calls. Later on the pleasure was less certain. On a fine summer's day without many visits, it was great fun to play in a stream, or (if the farmer was not watching) climb a haystack, or wrestle a sheep. Moreover some of the farmers' wives gave us sweets or buns. Sometimes, however, particularly in the winter when the weather was bad and my father was busy, it was a miserable bore – moving quickly from house to house in dreary damp villages, wanting to go home, and getting more hungry as lunch time went past hour by hour until 2 or 3 pm. On a good day there might be six or eight visits; on a bad one there might be twenty. The rounds were spread over an area of about twenty miles westwards up the dale and about ten miles from north to south. We zig-zagged through the country lanes trying to work out a route which was a compromise between the least travelling and the urgency of the different patients. As I have said, the pleasure was uncertain. On the whole Sunday was both inescapable and pleasant. My father had no surgery on Sunday morning and he would only visit either the more seriously ill or those whom he liked. The alternative to going out with him was to go to church with Grandma! In the holidays, though, especially Christmas or Easter when the weather was bad and there were epidemics of measles, flu, and pneumonia, things could be very trying. If Father came

Published in part in the *British Medical Journal*, 1979; ii: 1667–70.

pounding in after morning surgery saying, "Who's coming on rounds?" my brother and I knew what he meant – gates to be opened. The ultimate in both pleasure and misery was a place my brother and I still refer to as "Seven Gates". These were on a track that led to a number of farms a few miles from Fountains Abbey. To appreciate the meaning of gates to a country doctor, one must do some arithmetic. My father, being a country man, strictly observed the unwritten rule that a closed gate meant that the gate must be closed; there were livestock in the fields. Seven gates there and seven gates back makes fourteen: getting out of the car to open the gates and getting out of the car to close the gates makes twenty eight: getting in and out of the car makes fifty six. My father was a big man and he had a bad back so squeezing into the driver's seat under the steering wheel of Morrises and Austins in the mid-1930s was a trial. Having someone to open the gates relieved him of this ordeal and greatly speeded up his whole day's work.

The cars at that time were not only small, they were also low slung. The farmers had no cars and were indifferent to the state of the tracks, which usually had a deep rut on each side made by cart wheels and a high ridge in the middle that was always threatening to remove the silencer or puncture the petrol tank. The approved technique was to put the wheels on the right hand side of the car up on the side of the rut so it would increase the clearance. When dry, little driving skill was required but in the mud things were different. One had to choose between going quickly to avoid getting stuck or slowly to avoid damaging the car.

For a time my father had a driver called Wompra. I don't know his other name; there were no other Wompras, so that was all that was needed. Wompra had driven staff cars on the Western Front in the First World War. Of the techniques used for negotiating the tracks, my father naturally favoured the slower and Wompra the faster. Usually this meant that when starting along the lane to Seven Gates my father would take the wheel and let Wompra open the gates, making some excuse about his back. About three fields from John Willy Scatcherd's farm, however, the track forded a beck. There was a deceptively gentle slope the other side which faced my father with an awkward choice. If he drove, the car was liable to stall in the beck or stick on the other side. Wompra, my brother, and I of course favoured having a go at it. Wompra could then ill conceal his grin of pleasure as he crept through the water splash with the engine revving to prevent stalling should the exhaust go under the water. Then he would let the clutch out with a bang and shoot up the other side, slithering from side to side like Timo Maakinen on an Alpine section in the Monte Carlo Rally. Usually though, to our disappointment, Pa would play chicken and adopt the only remaining alternative – to walk the remaining half mile to the farm house. This choice was not unreasonable because to get stuck there would waste an hour and to break a spring would really be a disaster. Once when Pa had disappeared we persuaded Wompra that the conditions were really not too bad and we would get back earlier for lunch if we went after Pa. We got through the beck but got stuck on the other side. With frenzied shoving, the help of old sacks which were always carried for this eventuality, and some heavy stones we managed to get unstuck and back across the beck before Pa reappeared. When he asked why we were so muddy we told him the car had got stuck while Wompra was turning it round to go back along the lane. On that occasion I think Pa was too busy and tired to doubt us.

When he chose to walk Pa was faced with the further problem of deciding which bag to take. There were four bags: firstly a medical bag full of syringes and pills with a sphygmomanometer, a urine testing kit, and an auriscope for looking in ears. There was no ophthalmoscope but then in country practice it is much more important to be able to see the outside of the ear drum than the inside of the eye. Secondly there was a surgical bag with a portable steriliser which could be put on the kitchen stove or boiled on a spirit lamp. There were also the usual surgical instruments, anaesthetic gauze, chloroform, and ether. Thirdly there was the "midder" bag, which also contained equipment for anaesthesia, and my father's beloved forceps which he had had since his time at the Rotunda. These three bags were all heavy. The fourth and only light bag simply contained a stethoscope, some prescription pads, and the most commonly needed pills.

With John Willy Scatcherd's family of five and the unclear messages brought into the village by one of the children and telephoned into the surgery, it was not always easy to know what problem was to be faced. Furthermore, there was a good chance that other problems in the family would be brought out for the doctor "while you happen to be here". If the weather was very bad and the beck was too high to be forded, John Willy (he was always John Willy to distinguish him from several eponymous cousins and uncles) would come down on the tractor. At the time of this story, however, John Willy himself was the patient. He had lobar penumonia.

In those days lobar pneumonia was greatly feared. It was a killer even of the healthy and was a great worry for the doctor. Usually the illness would last several days, with high fever, breathlessness, and lack of oxygen making the patient increasingly exhausted. The hoped for outcome was a sudden fall of fever, what the textbook called "resolution by crisis". There really wasn't much the doctor could do but my father's practice, if he thought the patient was becoming very exhausted after a couple of days, was to give an injection of morphine at night to try and let him have some sleep. Then about 1936 the sulphonamides came along and my father was trying "M & B", as he called it. For three nights I went out with him when he went to see John Willy and give him his morphia. It was late spring and the beck was high so that Father had to trudge in his gum boots through the mud to the farm. On the second and third nights he came back to the car looking worried. "His temperature is down but he's still very blue. I don't know whether to stop the M & B or not." On the morning of the fourth day, he stopped the M & B. That night he wasn't sure but John Willy seemed better in himself. The following day, Sunday, he came rolling down the slope to the car with a puzzled but contented expression. He pushed his trilby back on his head, wiped his spectacles, chuckled, and slapped his thigh, "God damn it, he's better!"

Nearly twenty years later, when I was at Johns Hopkins, Dick Shepard gave me a copy of *Eleven Blue Men* by Berton

Roueche. This is a collection of stories from the New York Health Department and takes its title from an epidemic in which 11 blue bums turned up at various hospitals in the city and how the cause was traced to porridge made with sodium nitrite instead of sodium chloride (common salt). The nitrite turns the haemoglobin of the blood from red to blue – it is then called methaemoglobin – and stops its carrying oxygen. Usually the condition is not serious and the patient looks worse than he is – but, of course, you cannot put up with too much of your haemoglobin out of action as happened to the 11 blue men. At the time, I doubt if I saw the connection but after we returned to England I walked with father along Seven Gates lane on our way to Fountains Abbey. I reminded him of this story and he told me that later he had learned from the drug company rep that M & B sometimes made patients go blue ("something to do with haemoglobin") and that if it happened you should stop the drug. "There were some others besides John Willy who went blue and I didn't know whether it was the pneumonia or the M & B. Usually I kept the drug on. You felt so helpless; there wasn't really anything else you could do for pneumonia; but sometimes it was damn worrying."

Appearances of my father

However prolonged and close the contact, I remember the physical appearance of people as in a sequence of still pictures, the sense of action being provided by non-visual memory. So here are three of these frozen images of my father taken from my first to my last memories of him.

HIS FIRST APPEARANCE IN MY MEMORY

I remember a figure wearing a cloth cap and a dark coat, sitting to my right and somewhat above me on a motor bicycle, gripping the handlebars and smiling around clenched teeth. A big wheel beside me is going round and round as I sit in the sidecar clenching the bar in front of me. Bumps, puddles, and splashes. Everything around us is grey but it is not actually raining.

HIS PRIME APPEARANCE IN MY MEMORY

A large figure in a brown coat of a raglan cut which emphasises the slope of his massive shoulders. Around his throat an Ancient Campbell tartan scarf worn carelessly – tucked in on the right, flopping loosely on the left. On his head a fawn trilby whose broad unrolled brim slopes gently and straight without a hint of a roll. A 'twenties hat, not a 'forties hat. In his right hand he is carrying a brown rectangular bag about 15 × 9 × 5 inches. He picks his way through the puddles and mud with a rolling gait but without the outward, duck-like turn of the feet which is usual in people with flat feet. In any case I cannot see his feet because they are encased in heavy brogues.

Although I do not see them, I know that under the coat and scarf he is wearing a floppy bow tie with brown polka dots and a loose-fitting brown suit. This is well made but despite the attentions of Mother's iron has failed to hold the creases it should have and is showing the creases it should not have. The seat of his pants is shined by thousands of polishings from car seats (see *Seven Gates*). As he flops into the driver's seat of the car, he throws his hat carelessly in the back seat but carefully puts the case on the floor behind him. I notice his tonsured head, large face, and short thick neck, which merges with a double chin hiding a determined jaw. His mouth is thin. If he really opens it in one of his very rare laughs, one sees good but obviously false teeth. His nose is prominent, with a bump on the bridge, said by him to be the sign of a Campbell. His kindly hazel eyes see the world through bifocals with heavy tortoiseshell frames. His eyes can rapidly change from worry to laughter without the rest of his face following suit.

His forehead is generously wrinkled. His eyebrows are bushy and if unplucked would meet. The outer edges are long and wispy. He usually carries his left eyebrow slightly higher than the right. When concentrating on some utterance, the left eyebrow rises by an inch or more, producing a veritable corrugation on that side of his forehead. When contemplating such an utterance, he tilts his head back and plucks the skin of the lower chin. The overall effect is usually glum but can light up and suggest a Robert Morley playing Friar Tuck in modern dress.

HIS LAST APPEARANCE IN MY MEMORY

He is lying at forty five degrees in a cunning bed whose position is infinitely variable – standard today in North American hospitals, but exotic in the late 'fifties in an English home. I am on his right. My mother (he now calls her "Clare" rather than "woman" which is the only term I've ever heard him use heretofore) occasionally comes in and fusses but for the first time in my memory, he is nice to her. I am encouraging him to reminisce and thereby document the family tree which I record on a large piece of soft paper. He twits at me: "I know why you're doing this, but you'd better hurry up. Glad that at last you're showing some interest in where you came from. I didn't like most of my relatives but the family is grand." Clouds occasionally pass across his face as he has spasms of pain in his right loin. A spasm starts with a clenching of the jaw and peaks with a closure of the eyes.

The spasms are so frequent that we decide to adjust the position of the tube draining his right kidney. He is to lean forward, Mother is to support him, and I am going to change the position of the tube ("In or out?", "Up or down?", "Try anything but, for God's sake, do it slowly.")

As a preliminary, Mother undoes his pyjama jacket and I pull it, first off his right arm then off his left. After this exertion he asks to be allowed to lie back for a minute before I proceed.

The final picture freeze-dries in my memory. He has no shoulders; his ribs are showing; his skin is sagging; his skin is yellowish; there are sickly pink naevi all over his chest; he has pendulous unicoid breasts; his belly is bulging.

No, of course, I have one more memory which I had forgotten when I started this chapter. He is in his coffin. His cheeks are padded out with cotton wool and his face is made up. It is a disgusting cosmetic humiliation. I turned away as soon as I saw him but not soon enough to abort the memory.

I am sorry that I did not realise they were going to do this to him. Mother had simply put the funeral in the hands of a reputable undertaker.

But perhaps the story can be said to have a happy ending in that he would have approved of my reaction because he had always trained me to "face the facts".

Mother in war – when "high" and "low"

I wrote a "high" version first and then lost it. A year later, when a bit depressed, I wrote the "low" version. '*Mother in war, when "high"*' turned up in an improbable place another eighteen months later. There are a few discrepancies between the two versions in places and dates. I could probably have got rid of them by a little research but what would be the point?

MOTHER IN WAR – WHEN "HIGH"

I don't know if I am unique but my mother escaped the usual judgments one passes on women. It never occurred to me to wonder if she was kind, beautiful, or intelligent: she was just Mother.

She was born rather late in life to the rector of Rathvilly, a small parish in Carlow some fifty miles south of Dublin. She had one much older sister Gladys who died of diabetes before the First War while training to be an opera singer in Paris. I remember my mother recounting that she had been told that at times Gladys' thirst was such that she would willingly have drunk from the puddles of the Paris streets.

I don't know what education Mother had but it was certainly not extensive and I think she relapsed into the Anglo-Irish life of the rector's daughter at about age fifteen round about the time my father became curate at Rathvilly in 1911. I imagine she was a kind, pretty, but rather silly girl.

From the time my memories of her begin she was large, bordering on obese. Her bosom was ample and she carried her bottom sloping prominently upward so that her waist sloped downward and forward. In summer she wore large floral prints and in winter a sensible skirt with a twin set and a single string of pearls. Her face was attractive except for her mouth which was deformed by two buck teeth that dominated her smile.

She was terrified of my father and attempted to run the house in such a way that nothing interfered with his conduct of the practice. She was up early and supervised the maids in the preparation of his breakfast, which was always the same: grapefruit (even in wartime she managed to get canned segments), porridge, an egg with two rashers of bacon, and toast and marmalade. Breakfast was eaten in the dining room and after it Father would go off to one of the surgeries and his house calls, returning later in the morning to see private patients. By this time the dining room had been converted with great fussing into a waiting room complete with *The Times*, The *Illustrated London News*, *Queen*, *House and Garden*, etc.

Lunch was also taken separately. Father had his on a tray in his office while we ate upstairs in a small room beside the drawing room. Then there would be another surgery during which we had to be as quiet as mice.

The most conspicuous feature of Mother's character was a peculiar mixture of generosity and snobbery. She spent almost nothing on herself but always made sure that my brother and I were well turned out. She did this only by going to the expensive shops. I remember there was a school outfitters called Allens where she insisted on buying our clothes. She wouldn't be seen dead shopping in Montague Burtons or Marks and Spencer. She would always do the food shopping in Standings, never in the Co-op.

Mother really loved the war. Each morning she would go on a shopping expedition which was interrupted by frequent meetings with friends in groups of one to as many as four. Usually the conversation took place in the street but often in the coffee shops, which abounded in Harrogate.

The highlight of her week was Saturday night when she ran an open house for the servicemen she had somehow come to know through her various good works. Usually there were ministry men or young trainees waiting to be posted but she also found a goodly number of bomber crews from the aerodromes to the east of Harrogate – Dishforth, Topcliffe, and Leeming. As the war rolled on these were increasingly staffed by non-Brits, chiefly Canadians, and many a DFC ribbon was to be seen. The girls were better class girls from the ministries. The activities were table tennis and a little dancing, and beer, tea, and cakes were served. I think that Saturday night must have met a need because the airmen came back repeatedly and there was a steady flow of Christmas cards after the war.

The only time we all met as a family was at the evening meal. I have described the tension of this earlier. In 1948, with the war over, my brother and I away, and my father having a desultory and probably platonic affair with an attractive widow, the marriage really came apart and it fell to my lot in the spring of 1949 to separate my parents and bring Mother south where she lived in a number of crummy flats between Belsize Park and Hampstead. Typically, she took no legal advice and I think my father grossly undersupported her.

In late 1958 when it was clear that Father was dying he insisted that she came back. I resisted this suggestion because I thought that if she irritated him when he was well she would now trouble him doubly. Furthermore she had always been a fussy rather than an efficient nurse. Father insisted, however, and she agreed, so when Father left hospital with his tubes draining his kidneys, she was at home ready to look after him. The last four or five months of their life together was a real Darby and Joan story. He died peacefully in her arms.

After Father's death it turned out that he was a rather wealthy man and Mother had a few pleasant years indulging herself in the creature comforts and taking annual cruises until she died of a stroke at the age of seventy.

MOTHER IN WAR – WHEN "LOW"

The striking features about Mother were that she was large, good looking and had a strong Irish accent. She was carried

38

on big bones and had a pronounced forward bend in her spine which thrust her bosom forward and her bottom backward. She stood and walked with her feet turned out, always wearing "sensible" shoes. Her head and face were round, a shape that she tended to exaggerate by wearing her hair with a curl all the way round its bottom. She used little make up but would make quite a "to do" about powdering her face before going out. Her shape made dressing difficult. In summer she favoured loose floral linen or cotton dresses; in winter a twin set and woollen skirt. Perennially, there was a single string of pearls lying comfortably on her upper chest. Colours were always mute – pink, pale blue, and lemon. The main features of her face were almost beautiful apart from her mouth: kind blue-grey eyes; a slightly snub nose marred in later years by a wart in the fold where it met the cheek; and fine peaches and cream complexion. Her mouth, however, was thrust forward by two, prominent, upper front teeth which leapt out when she smiled and spoiled her near-beauty.

Growing up, I did not notice her speech but latterly I realised how heavy was her brogue and why it caused her to be so strongly identified as Irish.

She rose early, had a cup of tea, and then fussed over the maids, who were quite capable of getting breakfast without her. She was particularly concerned to get Father's breakfast but she didn't go near him, she stayed in the kitchen until he had left for his morning surgery. Then she would flap round one room or another with a duster, chivvy the maids, and have a cup of coffee before going out shopping. This daily shopping trip was probably unnecessary, even before the war, but it was the only outlet for her natural gregariousness as visitors to the house were rare.

The town was well suited to this daily adventure. A hundred yards down the hill was the start of one of the main streets, Parliament, which climbed up to the cenotaph-obelisk, the town centre. The two other main shopping streets ended in a rather pretentious circle around the cenotaph. Mother's favourite shops were dotted throughout this area. The area itself was not great, so by good timing and a judiciously erratic route, Mother would "bump into" plenty of women doing the same thing. I don't know how many of these women wanted to meet Mother, probably many didn't. But she seemed to want to meet everybody and stand and gossip and possibly have others join in until there was a little knot, all with handbags under one arm and shopping baskets on the other hand. During the war this random meeting was helped by the subtle rules of queuing. A woman could always join a friend higher up the queue provided she fell back to something like her proper place on entering the shop. I know it was like this because on Saturday mornings and during holidays I was occasionally roped in "to carry". I hated the slow progress, the aching feet, the incomprehensible small town gossip but was usually bribed with some chocolate or whatever.

The women were classified by the shops they patronised. Mother went for the best despite the cost and the rows with Father. These shops were all small and private. The well known chain stores like the Co-op, Woolworth's and Burton's were for lower class patrons. During wartime the whole expedition was given more point by the search for scarce items and more spice by the uniforms passing up and down the streets. Eventually and reluctantly, Mother would sail like a slow galleon up the hill in time to "get lunch" for us at about 1 pm. Father snatched his lunch from a tray in the dining room but we ate upstairs: different food at a different time. Pa usually had a lamb chop (he kept up the supplies from the farmers in wartime) but I can't remember what we had except on Fridays when it was fish and chips and treacle pudding.

Mother was generous to a fault. I suppose she liked playing hostess, the grande dame. This role came out during the war when on Saturday nights we entertained a motley and changeable group in the large "ping-pong room" at the top of the house. Her prize captures for these evenings were exotic servicemen, preferably Commonwealth or American, who were posted to the town. Some had just arrived in Britain from training in Canada; others were instructors or advisors to the Air Ministry which occupied several of the hotels. The room also had a piano (sing songs were occasional) and a record player (heyday of Glenn Miller). Dancing was very occasional, was it too sexy? The staple activity was ping-pong. Mother always supplied a little beer and about 10 pm tea and cake were served. Father was sometimes there and I would wince inwardly for mother as he glanced at the goodies she was dispensing. Despite rationing she always managed to provide "something nice". There were upper class girls from the ministry and as people came several times, I suppose they enjoyed themselves. The prize guests were Royal Canadian Air Force bomber crews, many with the striped ribbon of the DFC, from the string of bases east of the town. Most romantic was the occasional Czech or Pole. I was in the throes of puberty and loved to try and get these heroes to talk about "what is it like" but they were understandably reticent.

Although the only bombs to fall on Harrogate were in the summer of 1940, they fell only fifty yards from our house and one nearly hit my father. He was driving up the hill for lunch when a plane flew towards him at low level. He saw three "things" drop from it which he thought irrationally were rubber practice bombs. The idea that the plane was hostile did not occur to him immediately but when he saw one of the "things" enter the road beside him, he realised it was not rubber. Fortunately it did not explode for a few seconds. He escaped but the car was badly spattered with bits of the road thrown up by the bomb. It seems to have had a delayed action fuse. I ran out of the house at the sound of the plane but arrived in the garden too late for the hail of rock to hit me. I was surprised to find myself unfrightened and for several more days was full of our "bomb story". It quite over-shadowed the school certificate results which arrived next day showing that I had done very well indeed. In fact my results were good enough for university entrance.

The war years were probably the best of my Mother's life. I doubt that the early years of her marriage were all that happy. Although there had obviously been something roman-tic about Scar Village, the differences with my father had started early. During the war both Brian and I did her proud.

I got into medical school and Brian gained a commission in the Parachute Regiment. Like many women she rather enjoyed the tussle of rationing. She also did her bit in the Woman's Voluntary Service, and of course there was the high spot of her week – Saturday night. She also helped Pa in many little ways to keep the practice going.

After the war, however, things started going downhill. Brian and I were not there to do what little we could to bridge the gap. The romance of the war was over and I suspect Pa got a girlfriend, the charming widow of an ex-patient. At Christmas 1949, Pa told me peremptorily that she would have to go. I argued but privately accepted they would be better apart and arranged for Mother to come south where she would be near Brian and me. I think she got a bad deal financially and should have seen a lawyer but to Mother's kind a lawyer is a last resort. She settled down in a flat in Belsize Park where every two or three weeks she would entertain my current girlfriend and me to massive Sunday teas of drop scones, griddle scones, potato pancakes, rock buns, and coffee cake. She worked at a local, well baby clinic, made some friends, and seemed settled if not fulfilled.

Then, in late 1958, it became clear that Pa was to go home to a miserable death. He had drainage tubes in his kidneys which hurt whenever he moved and which leaked and excoriated the skin of his back. The cancer was spreading all over his belly, making him uncomfortable and weak. Later it was to be expected that his kidneys would fail making him nauseated and sick.

I had expected to arrange for two or three nurses to live in but I knew that however competent they might be, Pa would want for "tender loving care" in his dying.

Suddenly, one afternoon soon after I had arrived from London, he said with a firmness that indicated how long he had taken to steel himself, "Your mother must come back. You ask her." No preliminaries. No pleases. His way.

I opposed the idea, reasoning that if she had got on his nerves when he was well, she would drive him mad when he was dying, but he was firm and so when I returned to London I went to see her. I don't know what I expected her to say but at least I thought there would be some evidence of the years she had put up with him. She said, "Poor Cammy, it's no way to go. Get me up to Ripon Road to be there when he comes out."

They got on very well and even joshed each other for the first time in my ken.

He died in April 1959. She stayed on and lived quite well on the money he had never been able to spend. She had high blood pressure and died suddenly from a stroke four years later.

Dancing beyond my means

In the winter of 1938 a neighbour and good friend of my mother offered ballroom dancing classes to our all-boys prep school. This lady had come down a bit in the world; she was separated from her husband and was struggling to put her two sons through a public school. For some two years previously my brother and I had been attending her dancing school despite my father's sarcasm, so it was natural that my mother would seek to support her friend by enrolling us in her classes at school. To persuade us was not easy. It's one thing to creep into a back alley dance class in the late afternoon but it's quite another to change into shiny black dancing pumps and dance with other boys in the gym while the rest of the school pointed and giggled at the window. Fortunately I persisted out of loyalty to my mother and as it rapidly became evident that I had a natural aptitude I was soon privileged to be the one chosen by the still whippy and attractive chief teacher to demonstrate new steps, and sometimes, better still, with her assistant, a cuddly blonde.

So it was that I overcame a problem similar to that which faces medical students – how to grapple with a body of the opposite sex without shyness or embarrassment. (Today of course when dancing there is less grappling but one still has to overcome embarrassment in making those funny twitches.)

I was even selected for a special duty, to be one of the partners at a dinner dance at one of the four-star hotels for the sixth form girls of one of the classiest schools in England. This was Christmas 1939, and aged fourteen, I was not only going to dance with debs but was going to have to talk to them as well. My experience with girls older, wealthier, and often bigger than myself had not been happy. I expect I was

pretty gauche initially but time, a "leetle laight dray waine",
and bodily contact eased things and two or three of the girls
passed from disdain through tolerance to interest even, faute
de mieux, to cheek to cheek. Their own conversation was of
course limited to what every seventeen to eighteen year old,
well heeled, upper class young woman should be thinking
about.

The evening ended quite successfully with the prettiest of
the party, in full length, lemon-yellow satin dress, and myself
really giving the last waltz what it deserved.

I thought no more about it until one Saturday morning a
week or so later I was hailed across the street by "the last
waltz" now clad in gym tunic, who skipped over and said
something like, "Gosh, that was fun. You're a super dancer.
I want you to take down our name and address. Never know.
It might be useful when you're called up." She then dashed
back across the road.

My masculine ego swelled because to commit that act she
had to break away from her friends and speak to a school boy
(both of us were wearing school uniforms with none of the
glamour of our last contact) and what is more speak to him
in view of the soldiers passing up and down the street.

The long summer of war in 1940 did little that was unpleasant to Harrogate. An errant German dropped some
bombs quite near our house. Some survivors of Dunkirk were
billeted at the golf club. From their remarks I began to realise
that war was not fun. And yet much of it seemed to be; the
Battle of Britain was treated by people of all generations as
though it were a test match. My father spoke soberly of the
odds against us but even he shared in the silly gaiety occasioned by the tally of German planes supposed to have been
shot down. Perhaps for his generation with memories of
1914–18, it was "eat, drink, and be merry for tomorrow...".

Then in the late summer the first signs of austerity appeared. Serious rationing began and all the iron railings were
taken to make armaments. Like many late Victorian towns
Harrogate's appearance was much subdued by this sacrifice.
Then travel was limited; it was not forbidden but one was
urged to ask oneself, "is your journey really necessary?" and

also to take "holidays at home". But "home" for many hundreds of girls evacuated to Harrogate was London, so to persuade them to stay put the town organised entertainments, particularly dancing, in a large marquee in the Valley Gardens. There was by now a noticeable shortage of young men to provide partners for the evacuee "ministry" girls so I was again summoned by the dancing mistress, and my father was persuaded that I was helping the war effort.

Puberty was in full flood and at fifteen I was no attraction to the typists from Tooting or the telephonists from Tottenham for some of whom dancing was not intrinsically entertaining, just a means to an end: the vertical exploration of a horizontal idea. Fortunately there were many who genuinely liked dancing and they appreciated my Astairoid skills. My favourites among these were G and N.

G was born in Soho of Italian parents. She worked in the Auxiliary Fire Service and although she would often turn up at the dancing in her rather rough uniform she was petite, supple, and darkly pretty. N was from Hammersmith but her folk were from Harrogate; she worked at the Ministry of Aircraft Production. She was less pretty but had a delicious figure and a lazy eagerness in her dance (oh how she could work her skirt!). The three of us enjoyed all the dances, even the old fashioned waltz, but our chief accomplishment was the jitterbug or jive, which had recently arrived from America. When I say the three of us, I mean it; if anything G and N danced with each other more than with me. On the dance floors of 1940–42 the couples were often all girl. I became quite fond of both G and N, and even had sexual fantasies about G, but she was being true to a chap in Egypt who was later captured at Knightsbridge along with many other local boys.

From late 1940 to late 1942 the war in Harrogate was rather a bore. Compared with the industrial cities we were very lucky but we had our fingers crossed whenever the sirens went because bombs well placed on several of the hotels-turned-ministries might have caused much confusion (or so we thought, probably wrongly). Then in 1942 the war began to take the well known turns for the better and the character of Harrogate changed. It still had the evacuated ministries and their staff, whose relations with the town varied from complete integration to suppressed hostility, but there were now two other populations. The "PRC" (Personnel Reception Centre) used several hotels to hold and polish the training of aircrew who had learned their basic skills in Canada or Rhodesia. These chaps had not seen action but they were the cream of the empire's youth (they were by no means only British) and the heavy losses in Bomber Command where most of them were to go gave them a sad poignancy. And they certainly wanted to dance with pretty girls.

Secondly a string of bomber bases had been established some 20 to 30 miles to the north east of the town and the officers and men used to come to Harrogate on leave. The aircrew with their DFC and DFM ribbons really pulled everbody's heartstrings. They wanted female company. A cynic might put it more crudely than that but I think he would be wrong. The girls told me how many of these types would hold them and talk spasmodically, and make only a desultory pass as though they felt it was expected but the heart wasn't in it.

By late 1942 the social pattern for all these young folk had settled into a routine. There was dancing at one place or another four nights a week, most particularly in a fine ball-room in the former spa facility where there was dancing every Saturday and either Wednesday or Friday as well. Now aged seventeen, but still no competition for the aircrew, I reached my pinnacle as a performer. In a manner of speaking I became a sort of pimp. How much did I make and what did I do for it? At best I made ten or fifteen shillings a week, four or five times my pocket money, but I didn't get it in cash. My remuneration was the admission fee for the dance (five shillings per night) plus an occasional beer. These were paid by the girls on the tacit understanding that I would perform in certain ways. These ways gradually evolved and to understand them one must recall the mechanics and formalities of the dance halls of that era.

The band would play three "numbers", one after the other, during which the couples would stay together and then

47

a roll of the drums or a phrase on the piano would signal the dancers to leave the floor. After an interval of a few minutes the cycle would be repeated. Each cluster of three numbers would usually be in the same rhythm, quickstep, fox trot, or waltz, but there were variations which we will come to later.

Around the dance floor there were some tables and chairs but only enough seating for a small proportion of the dancers the rest of whom stood against the wall or in the passageway outside the doors. On the whole the girls were static and peripheral while the boys were mobile and central. When the music started the boys would peel off from their pals and ask a girl to dance. As most of the boys and girls did not know each other and as most of the boys and many of the girls couldn't dance very well, there was much hesitancy. This was where I came in.

G or N or one of the others (in my prime I was employed by about five) would signal me to dance with her and would steer me to a part of the floor where she had spotted a likely lad. There I would show her off. At the end of the dance I would break away quickly so as to assure the likely lad that the girl and I meant nothing to each other. This routine and the odd glance often achieved the desired match.

Then I had extra duties during the "excuse me" dances, particularly the gentlemen's excuse me. I had to stand on the side of the floor and watch for signals indicating that I should cut in with my "excuse me". The reason was sometimes to rid the girl of a bore but often it was to free her to be re-excused by her preferred partner. It was an unwritten rule that one could not re-excuse immediately but must wait until somebody else had had a go.

So I got my dancing, saved my pocket money, obtained mild sexual stimulation, and helped bring female companionship to the boys in blue.

Mrs Mac and the Palais

In March-April 1945 we "took second MB". This is the second of the three great hurdles that London University required us to overcome before granting the degree of Bachelor of Medicine and Surgery (MB BS). Second MB was supposed to ensure that we knew enough anatomy, physiology, etc to fit us to become clinical students and start the three year long trudge up the slope to finals. Despite the mass apprehension all such exams induce our morale was high, we knew we had had better teaching than the other schools in London, and we nearly all passed. Certainly all our little group who had dissected together and worked together in the physiology practical labs, got through easily. We then had three weeks holiday.

I gave up the digs I had had with Madame DeR in Paddington for a number of reasons. Firstly I did not want to pay for three unused weeks. Secondly the rent was going up and Madame made it clear in other ways that she wanted a better class of tenant. London by now was perfectly safe from bombs and was being invaded by civilian and military advisors preparing to finish the war and get on with the peace. The increasing number of Americans and the past bombing combined to make an inner borough like Paddington a seller's market for accommodation, so Madame's aristocratic ambition to be more than a landlady for medical students was not unreasonable.

I had hoped to get in with a few of the boys in Bayswater where there was a cheerful and less pretentious establishment

Published in part in the *British Medical Journal* 1979; 11: 1667–70.

that gave the usual (two meals a day and three on Sunday) for thirty seven shillings and six pence per week.

Unfortunately the expected vacancy did not turn up because someone failed his finals. A quick search produced nothing at all welcoming and I therefore leapt at an offer by my friend Ham that I should stay with them in Brook Green, Hammersmith. Ham and T had two rooms on the top floor of a mid-Victorian house and I slept on a camp bed in the kitchen/dining room/study.

The vacancy in Bayswater did not materialise and nothing else I looked at – not that I looked very hard – was as cosy as Ham's place so I am afraid I rather overstayed my welome. Ham got rid of me by having his father, who was an actor, get a list of digs from the stage door at the King's Theatre. Professionally, this was slightly underhand on his part because there were few landladies prepared to accept the intermittent custom of the characters who performed at the King's or the Palais for a week or so. For professional and social reasons, these folk kept unpredictable hours and their behaviour – though in terms of sobriety and celibacy fairly predictable – was otherwise rather bothersome.

Mrs Mac's house was further along Brook Green and its interior was much less genteel than Ham's. He took me round and we went up past a loo whose floor was slightly awash and which, despite the open door, was obviously not ventilated enough for the job it had to do. I was then shown a dingy L-shaped top back room which was in a poor state of decoration but had the essentials. Ham brushed aside my misgivings. I took the room and, with his pipe firmly clenched between his teeth, Ham helped me move the odd hundred yards to what was to be my home for the next three and a half years.

Mrs Mac was slightly shy of sixty five, or so I would guess from the life story that unfolded from recounted incidents. Any exact age would have been only an average, however; physically she was in her seventies while in energy and spirit she was in her fifties. She was a bustling wizened little thing born in Galloway who had come to domestic service in London and had even risen to be in the dining room once when King Edward and some cronies ("there was a lot of talk about his goings on, Doctor") were entertained. She had married a shopkeeper and they had done quite well until he died in his late forties probably of cancer in the liver. "He had been off his food and having indigestion and then one night when I was washing him I saw he was yellow; so I knew it was cancer."

They had no children. This had obviously been a great disappointment but one which she had by my time accepted, as she had accepted so much in life. Adoption did not seem to have been considered by her kind, nor did she have the vicarious satisfaction that being an aunt or godmother would have given her in her small hometown. She said that she had once gone to a doctor about having a baby and he had, "felt around inside" and said he thought that she had had, "TB in my apparatus." She always referred to that part of her body as her apparatus, pronounced "apparraatoos". Although I supplied a great deal of what must in all honesty be called "primary medical care" to Mrs Mac, I can really only guess at her medical history. She certainly had a persistent cough and at times her chest was very tight and wheezy, so I think I can say she had chronic bronchitis and a bit of asthma. I never saw an x-ray but I would not be at all surprised if she had had TB as a girl. Certainly once when I visited her during one of her winter admissions to hospital for pneumonia she was "on precautions" and I had to wear a mask and gown. Presumably someone had seen signs of TB in the x-ray. She also had big knuckles and bent hands which, although nimble, were probably the scene of old rheumatoid arthritis. In addition Mrs Mac had a mechanical weakness in her "apparatus" which meant that she couldn't hold her water. I suppose that despite not having borne any children, she had a prolapse. Now the combination of a bad chest and a "weak apparatus" is a bad one. I doubt that she ever told the doctors in hospital about it and in any event with her chest they would not have contemplated operative repair. The combination is also socially bad for reasons which need little imagination – coughing puts quite a strain on the apparatus. When her chest was bad, when she was going to sit down for any length of time, and when she thought about it she would spread a good thick newspaper like the *Sunday Express* under her. Usually she would remember to take it away with her after she left but often the *Express* was left behind in a sad state. The final containment of the problem, which all regulars in the house tacitly adopted, was to avoid one corner of the sofa so that it was always available for use, and she played her part by sitting nowhere else.

She had a general practitioner, a rather bedraggled little Irishman, who, on the two or three occasions I met him, made it obvious that he had an inferiority complex with regard to bright young London students like me. This I foolishly exacerbated when, trying to break the ice, I said my father had been at Trinity College, Dublin. "I was at the College of Surgeons, meself," said he and firmly kept a conversational distance from then on.

In today's jargon Mrs Mac was unaware of the concepts of "family practice" or "continuity of care". She made "episodic demands of the health care system", which meant that she only went to her doctor for "sustifikits." Once or twice each winter he was called (usually at night) to get an ambulance to take Mrs Mac to whichever hospital "had a bed on the EBS" (emergency bed service). This he usually managed to arrange without a house call as her condition was predictable. Mrs Mac's favourite hospital was the Hammersmith or as she called it "Jewcain Road" and it was as her Sunday visitor that I first entered that place which was later to figure so much in British medicine and my own career.

General practice in neighbourhoods like Brook Green was probably at its nadir then. The casualty departments of the local hospitals gave a twenty four hour drop-in service; the senior hospital staff were "honoraries" who were usually on the staff of several hospitals so that they established no relations with the local general practitioners, who in any case were not allowed to look after their patients in hospital and were not even expected to visit them. Indeed it was taken for granted, I discovered as a senior student, that all the local family doctors were incompetent. Unfortunately this assumption was not unreasonable in our part of Hammersmith. All the doctors of drive – and certainly all the young ones – had gone to war, and the neighbourhood fell between private practice and a good panel practice; it was not really poor but could no longer support middle class pretensions.

The house was dingy when I first went there and with the passage of time it passed through stages of grubbiness to being so downright filthy that when my mother came to see me shortly before I left, she was appalled, as indeed I should have been. The epicentres of filth were the bathroom and the kitchen. The lodgers really only used the bathroom for a morning wash and shave. Often three would be there at once sharing the two taps, one basin, and one mirror which, fortunately, was wide enough to share two faces. A third occupant used a small piece of broken vanity mirror propped up on the window sill. The supply of hot water was too erratic to encourage use of the bath, which had a broad band of deposit at and slightly above the five inch depth prescribed by wartime austerity.

The sink in the kitchen was a large shallow stoneware trough with one cold tap. Dishes were only removed as needed. Mrs Mac's technique was to slosh some boiling water into an enamel bowl, pass the requisite number of plates rapidly through it, and then wipe them with the apron she always wore. Fortunately this apron didn't go all the way round to her damp bottom but even if it had I think it would have been preferable to the greasy "towel" which also saw service as oven and floor cloth.

But for me the food was usually good, or at least plentiful. As the floating population ate irregularly Mrs Mac had no difficulty in using their ration books to indulge my appetite. Her specialities were steak and kidney pudding and spotted Dick but I remember mostly her Sunday morning breakfasts which occasionally ran to five courses: grapefruit, porridge, kippers (real Arbroath smokies), sausages, bacon and egg, toast and marmalade.

My room became a pretty conventional student's pad. Ham had given me some pleasant bits of bric a brac such as a large African bamboo recorder, an almost equally large Rumanian pipe which held half an ounce of tobacco, and two leatherette covered Haig dimple bottles (all of which I still have). I covered the walls with pin-ups from a series of colour prints given away by Punch: the girls were all very 1940s with high shoulders, red lips, and shoulder length waved hair (black, platinum, or red).

I had a small table on which, besides the books, was my main companion, a radio I had been given for my twenty first birthday. Every night I would look forward to "Midnight in Munich" on the American Forces network, whose disc jockey (a figure as yet unknown in England) was Muffitt Moffatt. The big band era was at its height.

The bed was lumpy but quite comfortable for one and would take two provided they were not there for sleeping. The sheets were changed about once a term but I got three turns of duty out of each change by first swapping top for bottom and then head for feet. This meant, however, that I had to learn a fresh way into bed each month if my toes were to avoid the gaps between the patches and other holes. It was only too easy to make what the surgeons call "a false passage".

I had a winter long battle with the cold which I coped with by getting desk work over while running the gas fire for as long as tuppence lasted. The colder the weather, the shorter the time. Then I would make a cup of cocoa, fill my hot water bottle (an old, stone, ginger beer bottle), and retire with my books. I wore my dressing gown wrong way round, scarf around my neck, and duffle coat spread over the bed clothes, which, in turn, coverd my feet. I cannot claim that I suffered as much as Ivan Denisovitch but his description of settling down for the night in Gulag X took me back.

Spasmodically throughout the year I would have to fight a three night battle with bed bugs. I don't know why their offensive always lasted three nights but once started – by a bite that dragged one back to consciousness in time to throw back the covers and see the evil, blood filled, little bastard wandering off – I knew that despite all my efforts I was in for it for two or three nights. Now bed bugs don't live in the bed; they live in the woodwork. My plan of campaign was not to crush them, therefore, that only made a bloody mess, but to heap DDT on their backs and hope they would carry it back to their burrows. I finally did discover from an ex-prisoner of war a trick that cut short the battles. I moved my bed out from the wall and stood each bed leg in paraffin (kerosene). Behind these moats I slept undisturbed, provided some guerillas hadn't camped out in the mattress.

The inhabitants of 67 Brook Green could be broadly grouped into five classes. Firstly there were two other permanents, Joe a tubercular Irish labourer whose week revolved around the dogs at the White City and a retired captain who came from the other end of the social scale. He was a shaky plethoric man in his sixties. I never looked him up in *Debrett* but I think he was a younger son of minor aristocracy. In his early life he had pursued the unlikely combination of the army and painting. He was not much of a painter but I understand he had become an "opinion" on the Florentines. It was his authority as an art critic that led to his tumble down the social ladder. He had been advisor to one or two American cities about purchases for their art galleries in the twenties and had put all his wealth into American stocks shortly before 1929. He now seemed to be cut off from his kith but perhaps he deliberately kept relatives and former friends away from his sordid digs. He treated me as the only other officer in the place and Mrs Mac made it clear to the other ranks that she recognised this distinction.

Then there were the medium stay clientele. At first these were military or semi-military types. The most striking of these was a Canadian staff sergeant who used to supply Mrs Mac with both Scotch whisky and Canadian horse liniment for her chest. She would occasionally come to my room carrying a bottle of this stuff in one hand and the *Sunday Express* in the other and ask me to give her a rub. It really was great stuff; her chest went very red and we both inhaled the penetrating aroma of Super Vick. I didn't know what it did for her bronchial tubes but my eyes and nose ran freely for hours.

In 1946–47 there was a steady supply of demob folk in London for "courses". The most memorable of these was a former petty officer in the Navy who ate steadily with a rhythmically clicking jaw and whose conversation was a steady tale of copulation. He was not particularly boastful but claimed that in a year at Portsmouth he had got through six gross of French letters which he had been given by a Yank PX man.

Later still came a succession of Indian doctors for postgraduate study. They were the forerunners of the flow that twenty years later provided much of the junior hospital manpower of the NHS. These first were very impressive. Most of them came from Lahore, soon to be part of Pakistan, but were Hindus. There were also Sikhs and Muslims, however, and I wish I had been sufficiently mature to have listened carefully to their long civilised arguments about the future of the Indian subcontinent. I am afraid I was full of radical anti-imperialism and had no sensitivity to the agony that was taking place as Mountbatten and Radcliffe negotiated the partition.

Then in the third category were the transients. These were mostly musicians, members of the pit orchestra of touring opera companies doing a season at the King's or of a struggling dance band that had managed to make the Hammersmith Palais for the week. Sometimes there were singers or actors "resting" while trying to break into the West End. When the money ran out they went back to the provinces and I don't think any of them became famous.

Each year, however, we did have a visit which in its way was a bit of class. This would be occasioned by the *Daily Herald* Brass Band Contest at the Albert Hall and usually a few of the senior members of all of the top bands – Fairey Aviation or Foden's Motorworks – would stay and the great Harry Mortimer would drop in and share a wee dram with Mrs Mac and the boys.

My life at Mrs Mac's settled into a steady routine. I worked hard four or five hours a night at least four nights a week. I also read fairly widely, mostly the sort of philosophy and political analysis that one would expect of a left of centre student. On Monday or Tuesday I might go with Ham and T to the flicks, usually the Kensington Odeon, where we would dither between the queues for the "bobs" or the "one and nines". On Thursdays I would either go out with the current girlfriend or go the Hammersmith Palais in search of romance. The Palais at that time was at its peak. Lou Preager and another twelve piece band were always in residence and there was usually another big band occupying the third stage so that the dancing was almost continuous with only sufficient time between numbers to permit regrouping. The girls stood around the walls, singly or in pairs, and I would walk slowly round trying to select one who looked attainable. In my leather patched sports jacket I was no match for the uniformed gallants of many nations, nor did I have much money. I learned, therefore, to avoid the real glamour pusses who would rebuff me with the conventional brush off, "I'm waiting for my friend" (pronounced frayned). I could dance pretty well, however, so if I managed to get a popsy on the floor I sometimes managed a pick up even if the pursuit occasionally meant a long walk home from Putney or Fulham after the last bus or trolley had gone. Some of these girls became "steadies" for a few months. Mrs Mac didn't mind if I slipped them into the house but left me in no doubt that she thought they were not good enough for me. "Why don't you go out with one of those nice nurses?" These were, however, difficult to come by. The 73 bus was a long ride to Oxford Circus; the nurses didn't get off duty until 8:30 pm; and the resident senior students and housemen had the pick of the crop.

On Saturday I played rugby and usually arrived back bruised and full of fish and chips and beer. The Palais was always a dead loss on Saturdays, double priced and crowded with too much better off competition, so usually I joined Mrs Mac and her friends at the Queen's Head across the Green. Another member of the party was always Jack, the mongrel who shared Mrs Mac's bed. He loved beer and would pester Mrs Mac as she nattered away until she put an ash tray on the floor, into which every time Jack nudged her she would slop some brown ale. By closing time Jack was drunk and if we had not made him too drunk, he would do his thing — jump. As we left the pub we would get him to jump over Mrs

Mac's stick a few times until he got really excited and he would have a go at anything on the command, "Here boy!" even if he often came a cropper. We would wend our way back across the Green getting Jack to jump over the park benches. Together with Trevor, one of the medium-stay lodgers who was an ex-Mosquito pilot with full RAF moustache, I twice managed to bring off something extra special to end the week. The front room was separated from the dining room by a folding screen which rested against Mac's sofa, leaving a gap about two feet wide over the sofa at one end. The front room was often occupied by one or two of Mrs Mac's special irregulars on a Saturday night. These were usually servicemen on weekend leave who "had the key" and it was accepted that they could bunk down on the floor. A normal occupancy would be a brace of couples. One night Trevor and I left Mrs Mac having a cup of tea next door and crept round to ensure that there was action in the front room. Then we slipped Jack into the dining room. This couldn't be done quietly but such were the comings and goings on a Saturday night that I doubt it caused more than the odd loss of stroke in the front room. Then we managed to get Jack to leap the sofa. He apparently landed more or less where we intended.

Mrs Mac was very sorry when I eventually moved into hospital but I went to see her regularly until I got married and went to the States. I'm afraid I didn't write to her much during our time in Baltimore and I received only one painfully written letter from her. On coming back to London we had a lot to do and although I phoned a few times, all I could gather from the foreign voices at the other end was that Mrs Mac no longer lived at 67. I managed to trace May, her niece in Camden Town, who told me Mrs Mac was in hospital in North London but would shortly be going into a "home" near her. I said I would wait until then and Diana and I would go and see her. This good intention was put off for several weeks and when I next called May, she told me that Mac had relapsed a month before. She had been delighted to hear that "the doctor" was going to come and see her. May had tried to get hold of me but for one reason or another had failed, and Mac had died. I wish I had seen her once more. Or rather, I wish she had seen Diana and me because I was the closest she ever had to a son, and I felt a sort of responsibility to give her the pleasure of pride.

One of the best consultations I have attended

In late 1948, I went home for a long weekend after finishing the final exam in pathology. On the Sunday morning I drove Father on his rounds. Shortly before noon we headed for a big house near the Stray. As we approached the last turn in the road Father told me to stop. He had arranged a consultation with Dr Curtis Bain at noon and wanted a word with him first. He said no more about it, but I knew the patient was a young woman with severe heart failure.

Curtis Bain was a towering figure in two senses. Firstly he was a very tall erect man and secondly he was a distinguished cardiologist by any standard. He was author of a textbook and a Fellow of the Royal College of Physicians of London.

He arrived driving himself in a small Austin (which was surprising as he usually used a large, chauffeur driven Humber) and was nattily dressed in a greeny-brown tweed suit. My father introduced me with quiet pride, "You will remember my son Moran who is just doing his finals at the Middlesex."

Curtis Bain enquired after his friends at the Middlesex, particularly the cardiologist Evan Bedford whose student I had been. There were a few more pleasantries and then my father gave his well known signal that business was to begin: he wiped his nose and pushed his spectacles up on to his forehead.

"Now Bain. I've got you here this morning for a very good reason and I want to have a few words with you in private before we go in. Ethel Woods is dying of heart failure due to mitral stenosis. Don't ask me about the signs of mitral stenosis, I've forgotten them, but I know she's got it because I sent her to you two or three years ago and that was your diagnosis.

Now she's waterlogged and needs morphia to get a night's sleep. She's going to die in the next few weeks and there's nothing you or I can do about it." (This was years before the days when the mitral valve could be surgically replaced.)

"Quite so, Campbell."

"I've got you out here for the sake of the family. I want you to make it clear there's nothing more to be done and stop them dragging Ethel off to London to see some beknighted man in Harley Street. The problem is her mother, who is a pretentious, meddlesome bitch. Herbert, the husband, is a weakling and is under the mother's thumb. The only sound member of the family is George, who lives in Manchester, and I have arranged for him to be here today. Now you can do your party tricks with your electrocardiograph or whatever but don't go suggesting that any new-fangled treatment is going to help. I've had a word with George on the phone and he is prepared for the worst."

"Quite."

"Well then, shall we go in?"

I, of course, did not attend the consultation proper but I gather Curtis Bain played his part very well. He gave an even worse prognosis than had my father, strongly advised against going to London, and recommended generous doses of morphia to relieve the breathlessness.

When they came out of the house, they chatted a while about some new diuretic which my father had used to try and get rid of the fluid.

"Good day, Bain. Thanks for your time. Make sure you charge a hefty fee. They can't afford it but the mother will expect it. They'll probably not pay my bill at all."

"Right, Campbell. Always a pleasure to see a patient with you."

Pseudocide

On the appointed day we walked round to Senate House where the numbers of those who had passed finals were posted on the railings. Although several hundred had taken the exam, by the time we arrived there were only a couple of dozen hanging around the lists. One of the bright boys who feigned surprise at having passed attempted to commiserate with one of those whose surprise had he passed would not have been feigned. "Bad luck, Sam." "Bugger off, Brian." Those of us who had passed then strolled round to Hallam Street and registered with the General Medical Council. On the advice of the sombre old man who registered us, we then wrote off to the Medical Defence Union which, for a few pounds, would defend us against charges of malpractice, a risk to which according to this chap we were already exposed. Finally we filled in forms of application for house jobs.

Interviews for jobs were scattered through the next few days and late on the following Thursday afternoon we all assembled in the front hall of the hospital. Those who were expected to be successful were nervous and mock modest; those who had little hope were depressed. Conversation was strained, jokes were forced, and laughter insincere. After an hour or so the secretary to the board emerged from the board room and called a list of names. He then lined us up in accordance with the seniority of the consultant to whom we were to be attached. When the roll call was finished the others drew the obvious conclusion and went to the pub. We fortunates were then led into the board room where before us was the assembled multitude of consultants sitting around a great table. Little smiles and nods were exchanged between the parties to the various appointments. Then we were led out. Some went straight to the pub to join those who were unsuccessful but I decided to wait until the committee broke up and then pay my respects to my new boss. It had also been my intention to ask if I could start the job a few days late so that I could go home but he forestalled me by saying he was sure I wouldn't mind starting on the Monday, five days early, to allow his departing house physician a holiday. I decided that I did not mind and then I too went to the pub.

My boss was George Edgar Septimus Ward, a tall, twittering man who wore a winged collar and who walked very quickly but whose steps were so short that he actually moved slowly. His eyebrows, his lips, and his fingers all fluttered. He had begun his career before the First World War and had learned to use the new-fangled electrocardiograph. Since that time his status as a cardiologist had not advanced and he was more comfortable as a sensible but very conservative general physician. When I paraded in my white coat to go round with him the day after I started he first told me, for the third time, that he had been prejudiced in my favour because I came from his hometown. Then, after the explosive giggle with which he usually terminated all utterances, witty or otherwise, he switched his demeanour and his voice to the serious.

"Campbell, there are a few things you must understand. Firstly I expect you to remain in the hospital at all times. You have no off duty. Of course, you may go out for an hour or so, provided you leave the patients in the charge of another house physician known to me and let him know where you can be found. Secondly, apart from my weekly round, I will leave the care of the ward patients entirely in your charge but if you have any particular problems you must tell them to me and to nobody else. You may of course discuss the patients with the registrar, Dr Pilkington, but his responsibilities are to teach the students and look after my outpatients; he is not responsible for the care of the inpatients."

In principle this delineation of responsibility is admirable but in detail it was difficult to implement. Georgie was so conservative that all manner of matters which Tom Pilkington and I regarded as routine Georgie would regard as "particularly difficult". Thus I found that a blood transfusion, lumbar puncture, and several sorts of x-ray examination, all had to be cleared with him. On the other hand, however, he really did not like to be troubled between his weekly rounds and would irritably ask, "Why can't this wait?" But then, as he reminded me, when he was a house physician simple venipuncture (taking a blood sample) could only be performed by a consultant in full sterile conditions in the operating theatre.

A few days after I had started the job a middle aged man with a history suggestive of duodenal ulcer was admitted after a gastrointestinal haemmorhage. He was shocked and had low blood pressure. I phoned Georgie and after giving him the details, I told him that I had arranged to determine the blood groups of his relatives (no blood bank in those days) with a view to obtaining two pints of blood for the patient.

"Oh no, Campbell. Don't do that. You may raise his blood pressure and start him bleeding again. Just give him some morphia and keep him quiet."

Late one Saturday night I was awakened by a porter with a note from the resident medical officer, an ex-major in the RAMC, to say that he was admitting an "overdose" under our care. "Get a move on. If you want any further details, I shall be in Cas." Casualty was close by so I went there first and found the RMO hard pressed by a number of problems which, as was common in that part of London at that time of night, were not all strictly medical. He paused and addressed me in a military staccato: "Can't tell you much. Brought in by West End police. Arrested this morning for pimping. Found unconscious in a cell. Nembutal capsules in his pocket. He's deep. Tried to wash his stomach out but no go. Try again, if you like. Keep a close eye on him. Give him something to wake him up if he gets deeper or loses his blood pressure."

I went up to the ward and crept in through the dark to the green baize table where the night nurses were preparing gauze swabs for the theatre and was told that they had put David in a single bedded side room. There I found three policemen, two in plain clothes. They were worried because, of course, people in custody shouldn't be able to take lots of pills. Furthermore it seemed possible that David had been left too long unobserved.

They added a few non-medical details. David had served a few short sentences for minor offences including burglary but two weeks previously, he had been charged with pimping – "living on immoral earnings". He had been released on bail but skipped to Dublin. He had come back that morning and had been picked up at the airport.

David turned out to be a squat, heavy man of about thirty, flat out on the bed. I could get no response to questions even when I combined my questioning with painful stimuli such as pressure on several nerves or pulling his hair. I went over him and found nothing except a slow pulse and a slightly low blood pressure. I was concerned because we did not know how much barbiturate he had taken or how long ago; there might still be plenty of it in his guts waiting to be absorbed. I decided to have another go at washing out his stomach and then, perhaps, to give him a stimulant. First of course I would call Georgie, not because I thought he would be particularly helpful but if the worst happened, I would then be "covered". There was no answer so I called Tom and we agreed that I should press on.

There was some delay in making arrangements for the stomach washout so I gave David some picrotoxin, a stimulant then in vogue for the treatment of barbiturate poisoning. A modest dose of this caused some twitching of the limbs and face which I didn't like so I stopped. When I tried to pass a stomach tube, David gagged and his head swung from side to side, so I suspected that he was pretending to be "more unconscious" than he really was. Then I remembered a manoeuvre I had heard about from a senior student who had been an officer in the military police. I knelt on the bed and with both hands, I grasped David's pubic hair and attempted to lift him of the bed. That did it. He moved his arms in a very coordinated way designed to break my grip and he uttered muffled but recognisably unpleasant oaths. I was now much clearer in my mind. He may well have taken an overdose but he was shamming the depth of his unconsciousness. Naturally he would not talk to me so I told him very clearly and slowly that he had done himself no harm and would wake up in the morning. I went to bed.

In the morning he was still pretending to be unconscious but after a mixture of reassurance and threats he opened his eyes and began grudgingly to talk. He was monosyllabic at first but soon became quite loquacious. He sat up in bed and crossed his legs; a thickset, balding man whose body was covered in black curly hair. He seemed to have no neck, his head being screwed directly into his massive shoulders. His thick lips sneered more readily than they smiled; indeed, even when I knew he meant to smile, he seemed to be sneering.

David was understandably defensive and evasive, trying to see how he could keep out of jail. He liked to talk, however, and when he was satisfied that I was no threat he opened up whenever the policeman left the room – which he usually did when I entered. His accent was South African, detuned to a fashionable Cockney. His speech was oddly pedantic in that he liked to use technical and even pompous words and expressions with only occasional lapses into slang or vulgarity.

Although his home was in Capetown, he had been sent to St Paul's School in Hammersmith and spent his holidays with an aunt in Brighton. Just after David had taken the school certificate, this lady had caught him rumbling the maid. "She told me if I failed school cert, she would tell my father. My academic pretensions were modest and I expected to fail so a few days later, I decamped with my aunt's jewellery and embarked on a career of crime. Ironically, I had passed school certificate but by the time I found out, it was too late."

For a few years he had made ends meet by petty theft, stealing cars, and a little "light" burglary but had then gone into pimping. "Nothing like it. Good money and safe as houses if you're careful. Unfortunately I got too cocky and when another girl tried to muscle in on my girl's beat, I threatened her with GBH. Her protector and I had a bit of argy-bargy and we were picked up."

He faced a term of seven to fourteen years' imprisonment.

Having jumped bail, the term was likely to be longer rather than shorter.

I was unhealthily but naturally intrigued by this denizen of the underworld and over the next couple of days I was much titillated by his reminiscences. Of most relevance to recent events, I ascertained that he was employing only one girl ("More than one's too complicated if you try to look after them properly."). He was very proud of this girl, Gloria: "Put one bloke in Bond Street with a fiver and my Gloria will get it." This boast led me to ask how much money they made. "Two hundred quid a week." My salary was thirteen pounds a month but this thought was buried in mental arithmetic at the frequency of the comings and goings required to make two hundred pounds a week at a job rate of three to five pounds. Hesitantly I expressed my surprise. "Don't be stupid. The big money's not in hustling, it's in special jobs – what in the trade are called 'wet whippings'." I suppose I looked blank so David explained it, giving vent to his penchant for technical terms.

"See, there's a stockbroker who lives in Albany. Every week Gloria goes round dressed as a schoolgirl. He lies on the floor and masturbates while she walks up and down his chest and abdomen. When he is near his orgasm she has to sit on his face and urinate. For that, she gets twenty five quid."

Later, I asked him what they did with all this money. He listed the essentials such as accommodation and cars which, for obvious reasons, they changed frequently but he could not convince me that these expenses consumed this vast income.

"Have you no interests or hobbies?"

He eased himself forward in his customary anthropoid position and said, "I have only one hobby – sex". But surely, I asked, being in the business he didn't have to pay for that. He squirmed to the edge of the bed until our faces were only a foot apart. "Sonny, I don't trust sex unless I pay for it and you would be wise to do the same."

During visiting hours on the Sunday afternoon I used to go round all the patients, having a word with the relatives and answering their questions. Last of all, and expecting to find only the usual cop, I went into David's room. There I found someone who I reasoned must be Gloria but was not what I suppose I had imagined. Average height, dark brown hair hanging shinily on her shoulders; features that could stand in for Vivien Leigh; and no make up. She wore a black woollen sweater wrapping a long neck and descending over noteworthy but not ostentatious breasts; an ankle length, rust coloured skirt held round a very slim waist by a broad belt; and flat, black slippers. A fifth form girl in mufti. When she spoke, however, her countenance and voice were hard. Today her accent would be fashionable: forty years ago, it was cockney.

"Pleased to meet you. Can we get out of here and talk?" I took her into the physicians room.

"I'll give you a hundred quid for a certificate to say that David has damaged himself and is not fit to go to prison."

I spent a few minutes gently refusing that offer without, I hoped, alienating Gloria because David had made it clear that he lived not only off but with and for her. At one point, Gloria burst out, "I don't expect you to believe me, but I really love that bastard." I wasn't sanguine about the stability of the pair but I had developed a soft spot for David and he was going to need Gloria in the coming days. She sauntered up and down the office, chain puffing and coughing and in between renewed attempts to get a certificate, she would go off at various tangents and it was easy for me to indulge my prurient curiosity and confirm David's stories about her earnings and how much preferable a regular clientele of "wet whipping" was to hustling on Bond Street. She obviously thought that the police would cave in on being faced with a medical certificate but eventually I persuaded her that the law would not take too much notice of any certificate of mine. At this realization, she went to the door, paused, narrowed her eyes, and puckered her lips and then smiled grimly.

"I've just thought of an old bloke in Harley Street. See you Doc."

Jimmy should be in the "Guinness Book"

In December 1949, I was appointed house physician in paediatrics, the "kids job" as it was known among the house staff. For the first few weeks I disliked the job intensely for a number of reasons. Firstly I had hoped to get the much more independent and prestigious job of casualty officer. Secondly my boss, Dr Eddie Hart, was an enthusiastic young man who came to the ward twice daily. Together with the sister he kept such a close watch on the patients that I felt I was reduced to the function of an orderly carrying out instructions often relayed to me by sister, who seemed to take pleasure rubbing in the fact of my ignorance of paediatrics and her special relationship with the boss. (My place in the scheme of things had been much more dignified with old Georgie Ward who only came round twice a week and would never think of seeing a patient or speaking to sister in my absence.) Lastly I found the patients perplexing, particularly the babies.

The range of conditions from which children may suffer may be vast but their means of expressing acute illness seemed to be limited to four: crying, fever, vomiting, and diarrhoea. Most of the patients in the ward were there for the investigation or treatment of chronic and uncommon disorders but there was a steady supply of kids with all four of the above symptoms. Furthermore I was on call after hours for casualty to which worried mothers from all over Soho and St Marylebone would bring their offspring. Not uncommonly the mother spoke little English so the diagnostic problem would be even more veterinary. Within a few weeks, however, I had mastered some of the basic tricks such as gaining the confidence of the mother and child so that the nipper allowed me to examine him or her. If, however, I failed to establish a peaceful doctor-patient relationship, I became adept at gaining at least a passing view of the throat and ear drums of a struggler. I also began to grasp how much more volatile illness is in kids. A simple throat or urinary infection may produce an acute vicious fever (plus the other three "symptoms") but a day or so later the child will be as right as rain.

The very small, very sick babies were particularly worrying, especially those who were unable to keep anything down and became so dehydrated (so deficient in water and various salts) that we had to give these by vein. Today this is a commonplace procedure but thirty years ago our judgement of how much of what to give depended on a few rules and a lot of guesswork. The boss had been an expert in blood transfusion during the war and taught me several tricks in setting up a drip, using even very small collapsed veins, in babies whose skin was all creased and shrivelled. Today in the Western world modern understanding of physiology, modern techniques for measuring the blood electrolytes (salts), and the availability and slickness of the nurse dealing with intravenous drips mean that few patients get as sick as ours did. In other parts of the world the problems remain but fortunately methods of treatment by mouth promise to do away with the need for intravenous fluids.

Although I made very few smart diagnoses, I was getting the hang of how to spot those children who might have something out of the ordinary, by which I mean illnesses like meningitis or abscess in the ear, and I was tasting the sense of reward which is so strong in paediatrics.

Although it may seem insensitive to the patients to say so, Christmas was a great time in the teaching hospitals then. Each ward was elaborately decorated usually taking some theme from pantomime or one of the current West End shows. Of course the kids' ward was special. For weeks, in slack moments, the nurses made decorations often of great delicacy and imagination. Early in the afternoon, three days before Christmas, the ward was being transformed into Treasure Island when Jimmy was admitted. He was eleven but big for his age and a bit simple. His intelligence was only such that he was in the same class as six year olds. When I came to know him, however, I discovered that he was very gentle; my father would have called him a nice harmless lad. When I talked to him his face was almost expressionless but his eyes were disturbing. There were small folds of skin like curtains drawn back on their inner sides and his gaze never left my face whenever I was near him. When I first knew him, I was unsure whether this gaze betrayed even less understanding than his simple answers suggested or, on the other hand, a mysterious awareness to which I was not privy.

Jimmy was admitted to hospital because for two weeks he had been complaining of not feeling well and of increasing headache and feverishness. He admitted to little else. On examining him, his temperature was 102 °F but otherwise he was in pretty good shape except for a suspicion of neck stiffness, by which I mean that he could not put his chin on his chest and when I tried to lift his head to help him I felt contraction in the muscles of the back of the neck. These signs were not striking but they were worrying.

His mother had for some reason been delayed but arrived as I finished my preliminary examination. She confirmed the slow onset of the illness and the absence of other symptoms but added one other clue. When I asked her if there was any TB in the family, she told me that a relative living with them some years previously had been in a sanatorium. This clue increased my suspicion that Jimmy had tuberculous meningitis, TBM.

Tuberculous meningitis means an infection of the meninges or coverings of the brain and spinal cord with the tubercle bacillus. It usually affects children, who become infected with TB in the lungs before their defences can cope and keep the infection localised. The TB gets into the blood and may spread to many parts of the body but infection of the meninges was particularly feared because it was nearly always fatal and the illness was horrible.

I say it was particularly feared because today TB is quite rare and we have special drugs that can cure it. In 1949 we had one drug, streptomycin, which had been shown to be effective in many cases but its use was difficult and uncertain.

Back to the diagnosis. We examined Jimmy carefully, x-rayed his chest without finding anything, and later that afternoon I performed lumbar puncture (LP) to obtain a sample of cerebrospinal fluid (CSF). This entails the insertion of a needle deeply into the lower back between the bones of the vertebral column. If I got my bearings right, the needle would enter a space between the meninges that contains the CSF which bathes the surface of the brain and spinal cord and some chambers within the brain. The inflammation caused by TB infection of the meninges causes the CSF to become purulent. This is only slightly so in the early stages but later on the fluid becomes thick and clotted and the meninges become matted. Tubercle bacilli may also be found in the CSF but often they are too few to see under the microscope and it takes several weeks to grow them in special cultures in the laboratory.

Jimmy was placed in a bed at the end of the ward and with the help of the head nurse I started to do the LP while, beside the curtains surrounding us, the Christmas tree was being decorated. We got Jimmy curled up lying on his side and I started to anaesthetise the skin, the idea being to use a fine needle to infiltrate local anaesthetic along the route of the larger LP needle. I knew the LP was going to be difficult immediately as Jimmy twitched at every movement of the needle. Eventually I felt I had the route sufficiently anaesthetised but I was afraid that a sudden unexpected and violent twitch might push the needle in the wrong direction or even snap it off inside his back. Fortunately I steered the LP needle in without hurting him and he was very good for the next few minutes while I measured the pressure of the CSF and collected samples. The pressure was slightly raised and the fluid was slightly cloudy. I pulled the needle out and turned Jimmy onto his back. I am not sure which of us was sweating the more, and in my mind was the knowledge that the treatment of TB would require daily LPs. How would we get Jimmy to have them?

As it was now late in the afternoon I took the samples over to the pathology laboratory myself. The chemical changes in the fluid were suggestive of TB but not unexpectedly the bacteriologists could not see TB. They could not find anything else, however, so our suspicions were greatly strengthened.

The following morning the boss suggested I do another LP to see if the chemical changes were more definite and to provide the bacteriologists with a second sample to look at and culture. I half heartedly murmured that another LP would be dicey but both the boss and the registrar hinted disdainfully that they expected more of a house physician than cowardice in the face of a difficult LP. Furthermore they pointed out that I was the chief believer in the diagnosis of TBM and it would be my lot to give the treatment, streptomycin, by LP every day.

So I tried and I failed. I managed to anaesthetise the skin but that was all. I asked the registrar, Tony Jackson, to help. He was a genial, giant rugby player who was normally tender and delicately skilful whenever doing anything to the patients. After a few mildly derogatory remarks about my technique he had a go but also made no progress. We retired but over coffee decided we really had to get another sample and at the same time give a small dose of streptomycin to see if there was any untoward reaction, a precaution that was taken before giving full doses of streptomycin. We gave Jimmy a large dose of sedative, therefore, and one hour later, with Tony holding Jimmy firmly bent to prevent him from straightening up on the needle, we were successful. Again, however, it was a struggle and when I was inserting the local anaesthetic Jimmy almost broke out of Tony's hold. Afterwards, despite being nearly knocked out by the sedative for a few hours, Jimmy was clearly in no shape to accept daily LPs under local annaesthetic, even with a sedative.

What were we to do? The boss agreed that Jimmy should be regarded as having TBM and that the sooner we started daily injections of streptomycin into the CSF the better his chances. It was agreed I would try doing the LPs under general anaesthetic but if these upset Jimmy too much, we would get the neurosurgeon to put some "permanent" tubes through his skull and brain into the CSF. Streptomycin could then be given without needles.

Christmas Eve in hospital is cheerful but doubly busy. Work is packed into the day knowing that otherwise it must wait until after the holiday and the preparations for Christmas in the wards are frenzied. In the afternoon, after trying on my costume as Long John Silver, I went in search of one of the anaesthetic registrars who could spare half an hour or so for Jimmy. I was fortunate enough to find a genial, ex-RAF character who looked like Sam Costa. He had already begun to celebrate Christmas and extended his spirit of goodwill to Jimmy and me. We pulled an anesthetic trolley round and Sam surveyed the problem. Technically of course there was no difficulty about giving Jimmy a general anaesthetic but we were concerned about the need to do it daily. Having anaesthetic drugs every day and being knocked out for a large part of every day was not desirable in principle. On this Christmas Eve Sam used laughing gas, nitrous oxide, but found he had to get Jimmy "very deep" before he relaxed. Sam kept him quiet, however, and I was able to get some more samples and give the first full dose of streptomycin. Jimmy came round quite quickly but Sam said he did not want to use gas again because there is always some worry about the patient getting enough oxygen if nitrous oxide is used by itself to get deep anaesthesia and relaxation of the muscles.

By now it was sherry time but Sam preferred a bottle of Guinness – a taste he had acquired at the Rotunda. He had now entered into the spirit of my problem and we discussed all the available anaesthetics in turn with regard to their duration of action, how good they were at relaxing the muscles, risks of accumulating in the body, and the risk of damaging the brain, liver, or kidneys. Our discussion took place in a room set aside for seasonal activities near the operating theatres and Sam solicited opinions from all his colleagues who came by for a bit of good cheer: that meant we got a lot of advice, not all of it practical.

Eventually, with a light heartedness which I later realised was always there hiding a steely professionalism, Sam told me that on the morrow, Christmas morning, before we became incapable, he would knock Jimmy out with a slug of pentothal but I would have to be in and out quicker than...!

On Christmas Eve the nurses went round the wards of the hospital wearing their capes reversed, red side out, carrying candles, and singing carols. Naturally one of the first wards to be visited was the children's ward and there they sang all the usual favourites. With the ward fully decorated and a large tree alight in the centre, the effect was quite magical and the faces of those children well enough to be appreciative wore a marvellous wonderment.

After the carols I discussed the plan Sam and I had made with the staff nurse. I chose to discuss it with her rather than with the sister because I was having a bad time with sister and expected her to raise various objections. Staff nurse told me that sister wouldn't allow us to do the LP until late in the morning because everybody came to see the children in the morning and Father Christmas would be making his visit. She also made a telling point by reminding me that our plan would leave Jimmy either asleep or groggy for the best part of the day. We eventually compromised on the early afternoon. I managed to find Sam in his favourite pub. He was in a most agreeable mood and I left uncertain of his memory of the arrangement we made.

I visited a few of the other pubs and several wards to wish those in charge the compliments of the season and then returned to my ward. By now the children were officially declared to be asleep and both the day and night nurses were waiting for me to help them arrange the centrepiece. This was composed of a palm tree and a sand dune ingeniously made of wire, corrugated cardboard, and crepe paper. We moved this into a corner of the ward which had been cleared of cots and by a liberal use of string and sticky paper, managed to prop it up. Then at the foot of the tree was "buried" someone's old tin school trunk labelled "Treasure". This we filled with packets of sweets for each of the children plus enough spares to make me feel slightly sick.

When all was arranged I made a last round of wards where I knew the night nurses and used the mistletoe with a gusto which was sometimes social and sometimes exploratory. And so to bed.

Next morning I would like to say that the children awakened as the sun rose over Treasure Island. In fact the reluctant grey of London's December light had not yet put in its appearance when I went up to the ward to look at the very sick patients and carry out the essential treatments and other procedures, thereby clearing the decks for the real action of the day.

After breakfast I was dressed up as Long John Silver. Using an outsize pair of surgeon's operating trousers, I even managed to become one legged. An old coat with brass buttons, a three cornered hat, a patch over the eye, a pair of crutches, and several "scars" completed the make up. Then with much "yo-ho-hoing", I hopped round the ward distributing the treasure. The idea was to give the children something to keep them quiet until Father Christmas came just before Christmas dinner at noon.

I usually feel ridiculous in fancy dress but I had worked myself into the part so I kept it up for the next couple of hours as I went round the wards. Knowing it was to be a long day I paced myself carefully by sticking to light ale.

Tony was our Father Christmas while the boss and I, wearing chef's hats, carved the turkey. Then after a flurry of play with the toys, many of which had been given by local shops, the children were put to rest for an hour or so before visiting time. I changed out of my costume and was about to go in search of Sam when he burst through the swing doors pulling a trolley. Staff nurse had prepared the equipment for the LP so we were ready to go. I explained to Jimmy that we were going to give him another treatment in his back but would put him to sleep with a needle in his arm. Jimmy, however, was much more concerned to find out if I had been that sailor who had come round in the morning.

Sam briefed a couple of nurses about what they had to do to hold Jimmy and support his head as he went limp, then we turned him on his side, got his bottom out to the edge of the bed, and curled him up. I scrubbed up, cleaned his back, and made a mark on the skin. Then Sam very gently popped a big needle into a vein in Jimmy's left arm and rapidly injected about five cc of pentothal. The idea was to "slug" the brain more quickly than is done by the usual slow injection; we hoped that the total dose and therefore the hangover would be less. The first part of the plan certainly worked; Jimmy went limp as suddenly as if he had been hit on the chin. I put the needle straight in and obtained fluid quite easily. Then I collected more samples and began slowly to inject the streptomycin. I was injecting it very slowly because I did not want to damage the spinal nerves by pressure or by the irritation of undiluted streptomycin when Sam asked me for Christ's sake to get a move on – apparently he had found signs that Jimmy was coming round. I protested that I could not speed up, so he gave another three cc's or so and we finished the job without further trouble. Jimmy woke up in about twenty minutes and was really quite bright during visiting time.

Sam was quite pleased with himself and I was very pleased with him. With minor modifications and increasing confidence we settled into a daily routine. Usually I struck oil quite quickly – the fluid dripped out freely and the streptomycin went in easily. Sometimes though, for no apparent reason, I would have several dry taps. A change in the route of needle would usually bring fluid but on occasion, although fluid appeared, it dripped slowly. This finding was worrying because it might mean that the movement of the fluid was getting blocked and that would be bad news.

So the daily LP was always a tense business. When all went well I had pride and pleasure but there were the awful sessions when I couldn't get fluid and the anaesthetist was getting the wind up.

After a month or so, however, the performance of the LP itself ceased to be my major worry. Jimmy was worse. His fever increased, the signs of irritation of the brain were greater, and the state of his cerebrospinal fluid deteriorated. We had not expected an early response but frank deterioration was worrying, particularly as we had not proved the diagnosis. By mid-January he was nearly unconscious. We tried another drug together with streptomycin, which had been reported to help, but it made matters worse. At the end of the month the bacteriologists had grown TB, so we knew the diagnosis was right. At this time, although streptomycin was known to cure most cases of TBM, it was still generally accepted that many patients did not respond. One Friday on the main weekly round attended by the boss, the registrar, sister, and staff nurse, the boss told me he thought I was wasting my time: "Go on with the treatment if you like, but I think the poor boy's had it." I lacked the boss's experience but I had avidly read all the recent reports on TBM and I thought there was a chance, so it never occurred to me to quit. On Sunday morning I turned up to do the LP but found nothing prepared. I spoke to the head nurse whom I had asked to help and she told me sister had told her not to waste her time. I tried to remonstrate with sister but she told me that she agreed with the boss and she had better use for her nurses than helping me with those miserable injections. At the time I thought she was taking the opportunity of putting me down but in retrospect I think that her experience of TBM and her disbelief in fancy new drugs combined to make her regard what I was doing to Jimmy as not just a waste of time but downright cruel. He should be allowed to die without suffering a daily general anaesthetic and an irritating injection into his spine.

I had to call the boss about another patient and hinted that I wanted him to give a clear ruling to stop treatment. We both knew that he would not do that and sister would not like to lose face, so we agreed that I could do the LP later in the day when the ward was less busy.

This uneasy compromise operated for the next month or so. Every day I had to try and find a time that suited sister's pleasure and when I could also find an agreeable anaesthetist.

Then, slowly, Jimmy began to improve. In retrospect the charts and graphs I kept of his fever, his consciousness, and the CSF made his improvement quite obvious but living with him it was angonisingly difficult to be sure. By late February, however, and although suffering badly from headaches, Jimmy was quite lucid and his fever was less.

Jimmy being a big boy had a bed – not a full size one but a bed all right – without the indignity of railings. Since early

February, beside him in a cot, had been Tom. Tom was seven and a cockney. He soon became the ringleader, clown, and shop steward of the ward. Tom was constipated. He had been born with a lower bowel that didn't work as there was something wrong with either the nerves or the muscles. He was stunted and his belly was bloated and occasionally his bowels became completely stopped up. There had recently been some advances in our understanding and treatment of his condition and the boss had admitted him to hospital to see if an operation might help. Unfortunately we found that he did not have the variety of problem that is surgically treatable and were trying drugs which stimulate the bowel. These were not very effective and every few days I had to clear his rectum by finger. This humiliating process did not affect his spirits. Once when I was struggling to reach a hard rock in his upper rectum he said, in a matter of fact voice, "Doctor, 'ow many times have I to tell you that if you stick your fuckin' finger any furver up me bum, I'll piss on you?"

Tom took a particular interest in Jimmy. He always watched him after our daily performance until Jimmy came round, and as Jimmy improved Tom would give me bulletins on his sleeping, eating, and playing. He even affected such knowing questions as, "'Ow's the fluid today, Doc?"

As soon as we were confident that Jimmy was improving we reduced the LP injections to alternate days: we were concerned that while streptomycin might be bad for the TB, the daily anaesthetic was not good for Jimmy. Fortunately his improvement continued but we really had little idea about how to proceed. In 1950 one or two years of streptomycin had become the rule for lung TB, so we were expecting a long haul. We had two particular fears. Firstly we were worried that a few TB might have hidden away somewhere in a patch of scar tissue in the meninges where the CSF, and hence the streptomycin, didn't reach. Secondly we were afraid that the TB might become resistant to streptomycin and would, therefore, be untreatable should the infection break out again. There was some evidence to suggest that infrequent doses of streptomycin encouraged the growth of resistant germs. In the uncertain state of knowledge of the time we decided that we would use three injections a week as long as he was improving and continue this routine until all evidence of infection had been absent for three months.

Jimmy in fact made steady progress but he was still having treatment when my turn as houseman came to an end. He had his last treatment in June but weekly LPs were done to check on the fluid for another couple of months. As he improved I made occasional attempts to do the LP with local anaesthetic. Sometimes, after a struggle which left us both exhausted, I succeeded but Jimmy would not let me do it that way every time. I persuaded him that we needed to examine the fluid "when the brain is working, not when it is asleep" and with this deception bargained for a weekly LP under local. Gradually his fear of the LP lessened and my successor as houseman weaned him altogether from his need for a general anaesthetic.

Altogether, Jimmy had about one hundred and sixty LPs, of which I did nearly one hundred and twenty. More than a hundred were done under general anaesthetic and for nearly two months Jimmy had a general anaesthetic every day. I think Jimmy or perhaps the team of both of us deserve to be in the *Guinness Book of Records* but medicine being what it is, I doubt our record would be unchallenged.

One summer six years later I was helping in the paediatric clinic because the registrar was on holiday. My part of the action was to see a long list of patients who came every few months for follow up examination. I ploughed steadily through the pile keeping a watch on the number to be seen but as they were all unknown to me I did not bother to look at the names on the records before the patients' time came. After I had been at it for about three hours I was completing my note on the patient I had just seen when I looked up to see who nurse had shown in next.

By this time Jimmy was seventeen. Technically, he was no longer "paediatric" but you would be surprised how old "children" can be if the paediatrician has a particular interest in them or their disease. He was not as big as his size at eleven had made me expect and had not changed very much. In particular his gaze was the same; he looked at me as though

I was a vague acquaintance he could just remember. He answered my questions in a flat, matter of fact way but if I asked the right ones his replies showed that he remembered much of his time on the ward, including Tom. He had, however, forgotten the early part of his illness, including Christmas. His mother told me he was working in a market garden. It seemed just the sort of work Jimmy would be able to cope with: carefully following instructions in the performance of fairly simple tasks. His mother said he really seemed to have a flair and showed an understanding and initiative that not even she had expected.

I asked the nurse to take Jimmy into one of the examination rooms. For a few minutes I chatted to his mother and browsed through Jimmy's case record which was several inches thick. Seeing one's own handwritten notes after several years produces an odd sensation. There are facts and thoughts which have been so completely forgotten that their existence would be incredible were it not for the writing, and on the other hand there are passages describing events which are indelibly printed in the memory.

Some doctors have the satisfaction of knowing that they have saved many lives. This satisfaction is more likely to come to those who practice in remote places where they are the only help available. I have admittedly saved a few lives but the circumstances have usually been such that, were I not there, somebody else would have done just as well. In Jimmy's case, however, I really do feel that he would have died but for me. Such a conceit was below the surface of my mind when I pushed my chair back and went in to examine Jimmy. His gaze followed by face as I went through the familiar ritual of examining him. For a follow up visit in a patient who had had TBM, it seemed the right thing to do.

Then, for no good medical reason, I examined his back. Up to this time I had felt no strong emotion. I was pleased to see how well he was and how happy his mother was and I suppose I was touched by her pleasure at seeing me again and being able to thank me again. But the sight of his back was something different. Not that there was much to see; just a few white scars where all those needles had gone in. Seeing that back and feeling those bony lumps which had been my landmarks in so many anxious LPs caused personal emotion to flood over professional interest. I had to go and find a room where I could wash my face in cold water.

.

What is physiology?

In April or May 1950 I received a summons to tea with Sammy Wright in his room in the physiology department of the Middlesex Hospital. I had known Sammy for seven years and was to know him well for the remaining eight years of his life but this seems the best juncture at which to write about him.

In a sense Father had introduced me to Sammy while I was still at school in the form of the fourth edition of *Applied Physiology*. (In passing, that says something about my father.) This marvellous book told the stories of physiology with no pretence of presenting the evidence systematically and when Sammy did give evidence, it was often taken from clinical examples or from what would be better termed "experimental pathology". No teacher of physiology, including Sammy himself, approved of the use of the book by undergraduates but we nearly all found it to be much easier and more exciting than the stodgy alternatives.

Although I knew that Sammy was only in his early forties, I expected a certain gravity to accompany him. I was a bit disappointed, therefore, when two minutes after the hour of his first lecture in bounced a short, shabbily dressed man with a large head carried proudly on a long body. The whole impression of authority was spoiled, however, by stubby legs. He fiddled with the water jug and glass on the lectern, then rapidly scanned us with an expression hinting at mischief. After a minute he asked one of the boys in the front row what he thought of the morning's news. There followed fifteen to twenty minutes of banter which gradually involved about a third of the class when Sammy suddenly cut the topic off and said "You are supposed to learn physiology and I am supposed to help you with some lectures. I cannot quarrel with your objective but I have doubts about my role. I most certainly will not try and cover any syllabus, so you can put those notebooks away."

Then he picked on a student in the second row and asked, "What is physiology?"

"The science of how the body works."

"Whose body, and normal or abnormal function?"

Another ten minutes passed without our seemingly getting anywhere. Then another change of tack and he outlined the way we were going to tackle physiology in lectures (optional) and practical classes (compulsory). The lecture ended with a discussion of textbooks, culminating with the observation: "One book I do not recommend but which will probably be of more use to you in the long run is my own. I hope the new edition will be out this month."

After lunch we went to our first practical class. We were split up into groups of four and given two projects: 1. How big is a medical student? and 2. How big is a potato? Four sacks of potatoes each weighing a stone were provided.

Sammy and the three lecturers in the department moved among us answering our questions with questions while the technicians looked on in quiet amusement; they knew what Sammy was up to. We didn't.

For the next year my relations with Sammy were cordial. He occasionally picked on me in his lectures to be the foil for some Socratic dialectic and he always seemed to take special interest in our group in the practical classes.

For the long summer vacation he asked the class to study their body temperature. That was it: "Study your body temperature and describe your studies in a report which should be handed in at the first practical class in October." Characteristically, he gave us no specific protocol – no instructions – but hinted that we might study the effects of the daily cycle of time, food, sleep, exercise, etc.

I threw myself into this project with gusto, borrowed a rectal thermometer from Pa, and took my temperature every two hours to establish a baseline. Then I tried various things. When I studied exercise I wrapped myself up in sweaters and cycled hard for half an hour. This produced little rise in temperature. That night, however, at the 10 pm reading, when I had been dancing for two hours (see *Dancing beyond my means*), my reading was 1 °F above baseline for that time of day. At midnight it was 101.2 °F; so I "discovered" that short periods of exercise have less effect than long continued moderate exercise, particularly if you don't drink and make it difficult to sweat.

I thoroughly enjoyed the project and was very pleased when I got my report back from Sammy with the mark "Beta plus" and many pertinent marginal notes in the famous economical writing.

Sammy knew that we were much more driven by the anatomy department during term time as we hacked and scraped our way through our cadavers and he therefore held the obligatory exam at the start of the following term. This was not a pass or fail exam, just a form of assessment and feedback. I always came over a third of the way down the class and in none of the three such exams did I get the fifty per cent needed to pass the second MB. One year Sammy gave the exam on the first day and when the results came out about a week later and two thirds of the class had "failed". There was a minor revolt from the students who thought they had been deprived of the time in which to bone up on the facts. So Sammy scrapped the exam and arranged another one. When the students paraded for this re-run they found that it was in fact a re-run, the questions were the same. They were surprised, however, to find the "facts" written up on blackboards all around the room and copies of all relevant books on a table.

A chortling Sammy said, "You can stay here as long as you wish but I want you to hand in your answers at my 9 am lecture tomorrow." Predictably the results of this exam were in general the same as the first – although a few students did much better, an equal number did worse.

Then in mid-term came the shock that determined my career. Sammy got permission from the powers that be to restart an honours year in physiology and he asked Eric, Ham, Buxton, and myself to do it, starting in October 1945.

The others were most enthusiastic but I was very reluctant to lose a year because I still thought of myself as in a hurry to get qualified and into practice with my father. I was convinced that he would die of another coronary and that would be that.

I wrote to my father giving him news of Sammy's offer and sort of saying that I did not think the extra year was worth it. To my surprise he phoned and insisted that I take the opportunity of studying any subject in depth and told me that physiology was the one he would recommend. So I cast the die, sailed through second MB, and also won the scholarship for the best student.

Eric, Ham, and I did a little piece of basic research on factors which return the blood to the heart and thanks to Sammy it was published in the *Lancet*.

THE BSc YEAR

There were seven students altogether in our BSc year; the four of us plus one each from Bedford College, Guy's, and the Royal Veterinary College. We spent most of our time in our own institutions but got together for courses of seminars and laboratory work at several of the colleges. I remember in particular a course on reproductive biology at Guy's and one on endocrinology at Bedford College. In both we had to examine the cells lining the vaginas of guinea pigs. At Guy's this was done by scraping the vagina with a recently heated metal loop. At Bedford (ladies') College the cells were obtained by irrigating the vagina gently with warm saline introduced with a fine pipette. One could imagine the old dears at Bedford mentally crossing their legs had they seen us at Guy's.

The highspots of the course were the essay readings, which Sammy had the lecturers attend. We worked on our essays over a month or so and then had to read them to an audience of half a dozen critics. This was by far the most educational experience of my six years at medical school. Indeed I would be prepared to say that it was the only educational experience. In the course of the year each of us from the Middlesex did three of these performances. Mine were on the coronary circulation, the genesis of the nerve impulse, and, a favourite of Sammy's, "Over the oxygen supplies of the body CO_2 spreads its protective wings". In a way I have spent much of my life writing and rewriting that essay.

The exam in May was exhaustive – six, three hour essay papers and three, six hour practicals. Towards the end of the last practical Sammy came round with sherry and told us the results. Buxton and the girl from Bedford had been given firsts and I had got an upper second. It was what I merited.

For the next three years I saw little of Sammy but whenever we did meet we had a brief chat, which usually ended with Sammy asking me to drop in for tea sometime to "keep him in touch with what should be in his book from the consumer's angle". Then while I was doing my second house job his wife was struck down with something cardiac (I never heard exactly what). Sammy used to visit her after the day's work and often came into the residency for dinner. I was the obvious person for him to talk to and we had several very deep conversations on all manner of topics. His wife died and shortly afterwards he had a coronary which really knocked the stuffing out of him. He rapidly became a cardiac invalid with I suspect a considerable neurotic overlay. He confined himself to his office and used cars and lifts to come and go. He was the same old Sammy when teatime came, however, needling and teasing everybody who came near him, including Mrs B who looked after him like a mother in between doing her official job of looking after the animal house.

RELUCTANT DOCTOR OF PHILOSOPHY

And so to tea with Sammy in the Spring of 1950. When I presented myself (there were two senior lecturers there already), he beckoned me in and gave me one of Mrs B's scones and continued the conversation with the others until a reasonable time to turn to me.

"How would you like to be in the department for a year or so?"

I cannot remember what I said but the answer I felt was "not much". By getting two house jobs and then the post of casualty medical officer, I had planted myself firmly on the bottom rungs of the ladder of clinical medicine. In retrospect I cannot say I knew where that ladder went, presumably a staff appointment at a good hospital, perhaps – in a whisper – Harley Street, but I was convinced my envisaged ladder was preferable to that of physiology and that after a year or so off it I would lose my place.

Sammy understood me and emphasised that he particularly wanted me to continue a clinical role in the hospital and to build a bridge between his basic department and the clinical world. Eventually I was persuaded.

My duties were not onerous. I had to spend two afternoons a week as a supervisor in a practical class and I had to give about one lecture each week. In addition, in my special role, every two weeks I had to demonstrate a patient whose disorder illustrated the principles of some branch of physiology. For my own interest I was attached to a clinical service, attending rounds and working in two clinics.

In hindsight the job was ideal; but I was miserable. Most of the students were ex-servicemen. They were not gratuitously unkind to me but my attempts to emulate Sammy's style both in lectures and practical classes must have been pretty gauche. Infrequently, therefore, but too often, I was put in my place by a cunning question or a smart answer which aggravated my insecurity.

"What is the normal daily output of urine?"

"One and a half litres."

"That's a good average – what's the range?"

"About five feet."

I also missed the hurley burly and responsibility of clinical life. Then I failed "membership", the examination to become a member of the Royal College of Physicians, which it is essential for a budding physician to pass.

One afternoon at tea Sammy said he thought I should do some research. I did not like this suggestion because I believed it would take me even further away from clinical work, and reminded him that he had agreed I must get the membership. With his gentle but firm chuckle he told me not to be a damn fool. Of course I'd get the membership but I did not need to know more medicine, I needed to think what the examiners wanted. He listed some examiners known to both of us and half persuaded me that the difference between them and me was not knowledge. He went on to point out that, given the membership, the competition for registrar jobs hinged on other factors such as evidence of originality. In some way I countered by saying that I had no aptitude for research. This was a truly held belief, fuelled by the sharp witted discussion of research at tea and the withering remarks of other senior members of the department when I tried to participate. Furthermore I was acutely aware of my clumsiness, a failure I thought would be unacceptable in the laboratory. Sammy, however, said he did not have laboratory research in mind. There were all sorts of things going on in the hospital that could teach us more about physiology, and in return he thought a physiologist could help to improve some clinical practices. "At lunch today I was talking to Tom Holmes-Sellors about the things they do in chest surgery. Why don't you go and hang around his ward and see if there's anything worthwhile to be learnt?" After further persuasion, this time rather fiercer, and a few days later I started to follow his advice. It's not a good way to start research: "go and see if there is a problem". It is much better to have an idea but then, in North American parlance, I was obviously not a "self-starter".

It so happens that Sammy had asked me to give a few of the lectures on respiration and, rather than turning to the usual physiology textbooks for my material, he had suggested I use a series of articles that were being published in the *American Journal of Medicine*. These were written by some of the brilliant men who had been drawn into respiratory research by the wartime problems of aviation, diving, haemorrhage, etc. The editors of the "Green Journal", as it came to be called had solicited these articles to encourage clinicians to explore the application of the ideas to ordinary clinical practice. These articles were tough. The authors looked at physiology in a strange way: they were much more mathematical in their approach, more numerate. I do not mean to imply that the physiology I had learned had been devoid of measurement but it had not been imbued with this new passion for quantification. I went to the chest surgery wards, therefore, with a vague understanding of this new physiology but could see no use for it in the dramas of the operating theatre or the plumbing of the chest that followed. I went through the hospital notes of all the patients who had had lungs removed in the past year to see if there might be some hints of Nobel prizes to be won. I had some idea that the heart and circulation might be affected by having to push the blood through one lung instead of the previous two and, therefore, that the pulse rate or blood pressure might be altered by having a lung removed. If there were clues in these notes I didn't find them.

I compiled a list of the conditions the surgeons were treating, the operations they were doing, and what physiological research might be done (but also why I could not do it). I showed this document to Sammy who said in a dreamy way that it was a very good start and I should carry on. A week or so later I again tried to get off the hook by telling Sammy I was wasting my time trying to do research in the surgical ward. He said very benignly that if that was the way it was to turn out he would take my word but would I carry on until I was sure. Having spent six weeks surveying the possibilities, I asked him how long he expected me to carry on. "Oh, I had no particular time in mind...but shall we say...a year?"

Secretly I was beginning to enjoy myself and had even spotted a small research project but one which I thought was too trivial to mention. This hesitancy was exacerbated by the second in command of the department who pointedly said at tea one day that the department really should not employ someone who did not have at least a dozen research projects in mind.

My little project arose out of watching the physiotherapists at work on the wards. They would try to train certain patients to improve the movement of one side of the chest in order, they said, to improve the breathing and thereby the function of the lung on that side. I was puzzled because the breathing muscles are controlled by nervous centres deep down in the brain where conscious controls cannot reach and the standard accounts definitely implied that breathing is bilaterally symmetrical – that is, both sides work equally. None of this is really true but it was what I and nearly everybody else thought at the time. If the physiotherapists could breathe with one lung, therefore, physiology would have learned something. If, on the other hand, they were simply using some trick movements of the shoulder and belly muscles, then they might be persuaded that they were wasting their time.

Three of the physiotherapists, including the most highly experienced, agreed to cooperate in a small study. Firstly we examined them with the fluoroscope, an x-ray machine which shows a continuous picture. The measurements I made were quite clear cut. The girls could suppress the rib movements on one side of the chest but could not increase the rib movements on the other side and they could not control the diaphragm on either side. This meant that although they thought they were increasing the breathing on one side, they were really decreasing the breathing on the other. Their treatment may well have been good for the patients but not for the reasons they gave.

To pursue the problem further I decided to try to record what muscles were doing what. Very small electrical charges accompany the excitation of muscles and by putting electrodes into or over the muscle these "action potentials" can be detected, amplified, and recorded. The instrument which does all this is called an electromyograph. It is quite similar to the electroencephalograph which records the electrical activity from the brain. There were two top flight research electromyographers, one in our department and one in the anatomy department, to whom I turned for help in learning the technique. They were helpful, indeed enthusiastic ("Fwilled to get some wecords of the bweaving", as one of them put it). My relatively simple needs were learned in a couple of sessions using a medical student as a subject.

We then got down to business. The chief physiotherapist came to the lab; we put recording electrodes over those parts of her chest where the muscles we were interested in should be, we connected up, and then switched on. To cut a long experiment short, we recorded nothing. Or rather, we recorded no muscular activity when she breathed normally and we recorded activity everywhere when she did her one sided act. We had another session attended by one of our two experts, with essentially the same findings. We reached the general conclusion that the descriptions of the behaviour of the muscles of breathing in the books (which were based largely on classical anatomy) needed looking at with the electromyograph. In due course this work led to my PhD and seven years later to a book. Over the next few weeks I made some recordings from the belly muscles because these are separate from other muscles that participate in breathing and their action seemed to be directed to expiration (breathing out) by pulling the ribs down and pushing the diaphragm up.

I made a number of observations which I summarised under fourteen headings and sheepishly took in to Sammy one afternoon. I knocked at his door and was told to come in. "Can I show you something?" He beckoned me to a chair and pushed aside the work on his desk. He read my report: not a word. Then he asked to see my records. Then we argued for two hours, at the end of which he circled three of my fourteen points with a red pen and said, "Write a paper about these." I was dumbfounded; I had not thought there was sufficient for a paper but three months and fourteen drafts later we agreed that there was.

Sammy's technique during these revisions was infuriating. Other than minor grammatical mistakes, he corrected nothing. He made wiggly lines under passages, sometimes with a question mark in the margin. Often there would be a long wiggle beside several lines with some remark like, "Do you really mean this?" When we met to discuss the draft he made me do the composition. He could at any time have rewritten the paper and reduced the number of drafts accordingly but his generosity would not allow him to.

I followed up these first studies with several more and a few months later at tea (if you meet at tea, coffee, or the bar you need few "meetings") he handed me a form, which he had already signed, registering me for a PhD under his supervision. I regarded this as a trap to keep me in physiology and reacted accordingly. He told me not to be silly: "You don't have to do it."

A year later I found I wanted to write a thesis, realising that it is a much more thorough exploration of what I was doing than a succession of papers.

After the thesis and its defence Sammy persuaded me to write a monograph on the subject. Again I resisted because I thought it would be presumptuous but I gave in. Sammy found a publisher, and of course helped me generously and humourously as I laboured.

Sammy was a strong supporter of Israel and channelled his efforts through the medical school of the Hebrew University. He was invited as guest of honour to a posh dinner in a West End hotel and although he didn't like that sort of occasion, was persuaded to go and seemed to enjoy himself. When the proceedings were almost over he dropped dead.

On hearing the news, my chief reaction was a selfish one; I felt lonely.

In the front of the book titled *Applied Physiology* but known to several generations as "Sammy" is written:

Rabbi Akiba (in Roman captivity) to his favourite pupil Simeon bar Yochaz: "My son, more than the calf wishes to suck does the cow yearn to suckle."

Bachelor's rules

Domestic and social life changed abruptly when I finished my
house jobs and joined the physiology department at the Middlesex Hospital. For two years I had lived in the residency
where the most complicated domestic chore I had had to
perform was to fill my laundry bag: everything else was done
for me. There was also a warm, available social life: students
and housemen in the billiards room or the pubs; nurses
around the corner; and restaurants and theatres within walking distance. Altogether a cosy womb. I left it for a resi-
dential club in Lancaster Gate which housed nubile, young
physiotherapists and predators such as myself under the one
roof. The house rules were designed to protect the one from
the other and made the place rather stifling in a giggly sort
of way. When Bertie Webb, one of the registrars who also
lived there, asked if I would like to share a flat, I readily
joined in the search. Eventually we found one on the first
floor of a late Victorian house in a terrace square at the
frontier of Paddington and Lancaster Gate. Bertie was five or
six years senior to me and a very popular chap with other
registrars, students, nurses, and consultants. He had just
spent two years in the navy and salted his conversation and
habits with nautical expressions which were codified in the
regulations for the running of the flat. The kitchen was the
galley, the sitting room was the wardroom, and so on. The
flat had two very spartan bedrooms, one of which was small
and had a deep sagging bed (no trouble in calling this the
hammock) and the other of which had a larger, noisy, double
bed; a gas fire; an armchair; and a sort of desk. For no
mentionable reason, we called this room the hockey field.

After detailed discussions we decided that the only fair arrangement was to change rooms every two weeks. He who had the hammock had prior right to the wardroom for work and play and the position of an empty rum bottle by the telephone in the hall was to signify whether or not he was to be disturbed.

Expenses were to be shared – except for alcohol. Bertie also had a car (a 1934 Morris 10 with accelerator in between clutch and brake) which, for a small monthly fee, I could use when he did not want it. The menage was on balance a success but was not as great a success as it should have been because I had little experience of living with one other person and I was too concerned about money.

The flat dragged me further into an affair I had embarked on with J. While a resident, our intimacies had been brief and clandestine but the flat permitted, even encouraged, a sort of domestic regularity with undisturbed nights, cooking, and general cosiness. Though I was very attached to her, I could not feel confident about being married to her, so the affair dragged on. I made one or two attempts to end it but came back for more partly out of conscience and partly because she was very attractive.

On non-social evenings I used to read medical textbooks to help me pass the membership and physiology textbooks to help my students pass the second MB.

By this time I was taking my first faltering steps in research and even getting some exhilaration out of the studies. I was helped by Sonia, the electrophysiology technician, who spent most of her time doing electroencephalograms on patients. Her initial helpfulness became enthusiasm as we overcame the technical problems and began to see what could be learned with the technique. Most of these observations were made on medical students and the atmosphere became quite heady when we got a good recording. "Oh yes! I like that; do it again – but more slowly."

Sonia was neat, quick, and personable but not striking. Still, she grew on me and after a successful session one Monday afternoon, as we were clearing up and examining the records, I asked impulsively what she was doing that evening. "Nothing", came back immediately in a most matter of fact voice. "I've a tutorial which finishes at half past six. How about meeting me at a quarter to seven; we can have a drink and a bite to eat and see what's on in the evening paper."

"OK. Where shall I meet you?"

The rendezvous was always a problem on these occasions. As there were not many places in the West End where you could reasonably ask a girl to meet you unless you already knew her or had a clear destination, I hurriedly suggested the front hall of the hospital. I really did not want to meet her on home territory for two reasons. Firstly if seen by any of a large number of nurses, word would rapidly reach J and secondly I did not really think I should be dating a technician in the department, not so much for snobbish reasons as for the trouble it might cause. I guessed, however, that the front hall would be pretty quiet at 6.45 pm.

I went to my tutorial with two students who had failed the second MB and were to take it again three months later. "They are both offspring of doctors from the school. Get them through the exam even if you have to tell them the questions," were Sammy's instructions. Neither of them was stupid or ignorant; one was shy, the other disorganised. The tutorial went overtime and I didn't get to the front hall until a few minutes after the agreed time. I looked hurriedly round and thought I must have arrived before Sonia when a girl in black sitting with her back to the window in the far corner by the consultants' club uncoiled to her feet. Sonia it was; she had changed into civvies but with a vengeance. Stylish and sexy, a striking contrast to her white coated, flat heeled, no make up neatness of two hours ago. Her hair, previously gathered into a bun, was now swept back by a comb on one side and on the other was swaying over her ear. Over her shoulder she wore a black coat which gave good views of a slim black skirt and tight white blouse. Her heels were very high but from the moment she rose and came towards me, I could see that she, and particularly her hips, knew how to get the best out of high heels. Close to, her make up was skilful if rather heavy in its emphasis of her oval brown eyes and high cheekbones.

I hurried her off to a pub away from the hospital, got us some drinks, and then went through the motions of looking through the paper. She affected faint enthusiasm for several of the shows and flicks but nothing overwhelming. Eventually she said that she would rather eat than grab a bite and rush off, so we went to a little Cypriot restaurant in Charlotte Street and ate and talked and drank until about 9.30. Early enough to go home respectably but also early enough to do other things.

She lived in Bayswater proper so I offered to take her home to the flat, stopping off first at a good pub in Lancaster Gate which happened to be nearby.

Abiding by the rules, I had moved into the hammock on the previous day but Bertie had been away for the weekend and I was not confident that he would observe the rules or the signals because Monday was not usually socially active. As we reached the flat I saw no lights on and no car parked outside, so I took Sonia to the wardroom, arranged the rum bottle, and kept an ear open.

The next moves are, I suppose, standard – radiogram, dance cheek to cheek, kiss. Sonia played her part in these in a relaxed manner and arranged herself on the sofa while I changed records or poured drinks in a way which suggested that while the outcome of the evening was not to be taken for granted, she was enjoying herself and in no hurry.

I was contemplating a move from the vertical to the horizontal when footsteps came up the stairs and Bertie passed the door. We had the light very low but the radio on and I trusted that these signs together with the bottle, would keep him away.

After a few seconds of silence there were quiet footsteps and the sound of bedroom doors being gently knocked on and opened. Then, apparently satisfied with this reconnoitre, there was a firm noisy sequence of drink in the kitchen, use of bathroom, loud closure of hockey field door, all designed to signify "message received; press on".

When silence returned Sonia held out her glass and parodying the lisp of one senior colleague she archly asked, "Can I bweave fweely now?" and slipped off those gorgeous shoes.

There was no mention of all this next morning. In fact an unwritten law of the flat required no discussion of social affairs unless they directly affected both of us. Nor did Sonia give any hint when we did another experiment that afternoon. All three of us were playing the game under bachelor's rules. Sonia occasionally hinted at an understanding with a boy from her home town who was with the army in Egypt and I did not relish an entanglement with a close colleague who was from "below the salt" (snob!). We went out from time to time and when in the lab, however concentrated and difficult an experiment might be, we were always able to enliven it by oblique references to the flat and the rules that obtained.

"Before we go any further, are you sure the signals are clear?"

No more Mimis

By late 1951 after nearly two years with Sammy, it was pretty clear that I was committed to the breathing business but I was still determined to remain a clinician. I therefore had to do two things: pass the membership exam and get a house job at the Brompton Hospital. In fact the second would help the first because I would be back in the clinical swim, and it was well known that jobs at the Brompton were not too busy so one could get at the books. Furthermore I would be free of the chore of looking after the flat. It is true that the flat facilitated intimate social life but memories of my first house jobs reassured me that love can always find a way.

Competition for house jobs at the Brompton was fierce and I had no local patron because "our man at the Brompton" was Dr George Beaumont who had put his weight against me two years before. I was not, therefore, optimistic and my worries were increased when I saw the competition at the appointment committee. At the interview itself I was on a sticky wicket when facing questions like, "Have you taken the membership?" ("Yes Sir, twice so far.") and "I see you are a physiologist. Do you think physiology has anything to offer the specialist in chest disease?" ("Not at present Sir, but I think there is reason to think it will.")

I think Sammy must have done some lobbying because I did get a job – along with an Irishman ten years qualified, a New Zealander eight years qualified, and a South African six years qualified – as house physician to Dr Beaumont (surprise!) and Dr JG Scadding. Although I found the difference between them a strain, I now realise with hindsight that they represented not just the old and the young, the obsolescent and the avant garde, but also the best of two entirely different approaches to medicine. GEB's medicine was based on clinical observation and precedents (experience) but JGS, while drawing on a wealth of experience, was a reasoner and would argue his opinions rather than simply handing them down.

Life as a house physician at the Brompton was much more civilised than that at the Middlesex. The building itself helped. It was (and still is) an early nineteenth century manor house whose floors (galleries) and rooms had been turned into small wards. Also the house staff were cossetted. I was awakened every morning with a cup of tea and my shoes were left polished outside my bedroom door. Although lunch was a typical hospital affair, dinner was quite formal. We assembled just before 7 pm in the common room (no white coats allowed) and were led to the dining room by the chaplain and the resident medical officer who, in my day, was Tom Wilson, a wry Scotsman who had won the Military Cross. After grace we opened our beer, by tradition with our spoons using our knuckles as levers to propel the caps over our shoulders towards the portraits of non-eminent Victorians which lined the walls. The beer was provided free by a brewery outside London whose trademark was an elephant. It was not very good beer but free "elephant piss" was better than none at all. The beer may not have been exceptional but the food was – at least by the standards I had known for the past eight years or so. Not haute cuisine but plenty of it.

My happiest gastronomic memory is of Shrove Tuesday when we were, of course, served pancakes. These were not crêpes but good, honest, leathery things that went well with treacle. Raymond, my neighbour at table, declined his and as a quick count of the serving table suggested that our ration was to be two each, I said I would have it. I already had a reputation as what the Irish call "a cormorant" and soon there was a chain reaction with bets all round that I could not eat the whole lot. As we had an x-ray interpretation meeting to follow it was agreed that a fair time limit for the orgy was "half an hour before closing time", that is 10 pm. Some of the twelve or so diners were not quite so choosy as Raymond, so the total to be dealt with ended up at eighteen. I got through six or seven pancakes with no trouble at all at table and then, bearing my plate and followed by Raymond bearing the rest on a silver serving dish (covered) and another house physician bearing a pound tin of Tate and Lyle's Golden Syrup, we repaired to the common room. While reviewing the week's interesting x-rays, I managed another half dozen or so without much trouble but the final stretch had me moving at a snail's pace. Nevertheless I won the bet (a pint per man, to be taken whenever I liked) and even squeezed a pint of bitter past the log jam in my stomach before making night rounds. I believe that for many years my only distinguishing feature as far as JGS was concerned was "the house physician who ate a lot".

As expected the work – at least for my particular two chiefs – was not heavy. Most of my patients were on Albert Gallery (men) and Victoria Gallery (women). Sister O'Grady on Victoria made the work even lighter by composing a list each morning, in copperplate handwriting, of the tasks of the day. Such predictability may sound strange but there was a steady rhythm in the care of pulmonary tuberculosis; examinations, x-rays, and blood tests were done at specified intervals. Sister O'G was of the old school. She dressed in the nurse's uniform of a bygone age – enormous cap, full apron, starched collar, frills, cuffs – and, although she called you "Mister" ("Doctor" being reserved for consultant physicians), she left you in no doubt that it was her ward.

A regular feature of life in those days was "the A-P clinic". This clinic worked almost continuously morning and afternoon and there was even a late evening clinic on Thursday. The abbreviation "A-P" stands for "artificial pneumothorax". Pneumothorax means "air in the chest", more particularly in the pleural space that separates the lung on each side from the covering ribs and muscles. The purpose of a pneumothorax was to rest the lung on that side by making it smaller, thus reducing the amount of air and blood going to it. This treatment was a local expression of the principle of rest which had been the mainstay of the treatment of TB from the end of World War I until the advent of streptomycin. This drug and others had shown their efficacy over the four or five years before my time at the Brompton but the drugs were still seen as adjuncts to rest or preparations for mechanical treatments ("collapse therapy"). Twice or three times a week, therefore, each of us "did" the A-P clinic in pairs. This was highly organised. A registrar examined the patient by x-ray and consulted his or her record on which was a sketch of what the lung had looked like last time. He then wrote a brief instruction of the volume of air to be put into the chest (and often specified a pressure he did not want us to exceed). The patient came through to us. He or she handed nurse the sheet with the registrar's instructions and then climbed onto a couch with the side of the A-P uppermost. We were "gowned and scrubbed" and between patients rested our hands in a solution of carbolic. Having looked at the sketch and read the registrar's instructions, we chose an appropriate needle, and using one of the several eponymous contraptions of pistons or bottles, "gave the refill".

The several A-P clinics varied remarkably in the number and type of case. The very old consultants did not make much use of A-Ps and the younger ones tended to use them for "well chosen" patients whose lungs collapsed easily. There were, however, some middle aged consultants who really seemed to have an irrational faith in A-Ps. In these clinics the patients might attend for ten or more years, having small quantities of air inserted into deeply hidden parts of their chests. One became very skilful with the needle.

In those days the romantic view of TB as a disease of the young still had more than a ring of truth and some of the women patients were very attractive. In the case of the in-patients this, added to their celibacy, could generate "heat" in a four bedded ward, which added spice to the ward rounds. One silver haired consultant with the looks of David Niven always examined every patient's chest, front and back, on every round. Privacy was scant so that this ritual generated an electric atmosphere which, on occasion, would be broken by uncontrolled giggling, behaviour sister O'G did not under-stand, approve of, or could stop.

I came under particular strain in the A-P clinic from a young Hungarian whose name – I hope for healthy symbolic reasons – I forget. She was exquisite: petite, with hips and very high heels combining to produce a movement which weakened my knees as she came to the couch. Her A-P was "new" so required refills every week or so and she had not yet become hardened or seasoned to the "refill".

I looked forward to my encounter with the Magyar beauty. She would slip off her high heels and hop up onto the couch with her back to me, hips deliciously curved. She would then raise her right arm above her head and grasp the nurse's arm and I would start the refill. As I fixed my fingers between her ribs and said "breathe in – now, out", she obeyed with nervously parted lips. Little beads of sweat popped up in her armpit and her nipple stiffened. I shot the needle in. The last two fingers of my left hand could not help noticing the delectable texture of her breast.

After about half a dozen times, I noticed that she darted occasional sidelong glances at me as I read the pressures and eventually, after one particularly slick performance, I dared to wish her "Egészségére" – the only Hungarian I know. (I am not sure what it means, but Hungarian patients always seem to like it.) From then on we became as friendly as the performance of an A-P refill permits and her glances were disturbing.

The real test came towards the end of my time at the Brompton when one evening I was waiting to cross the Kings Road on my way to a friend's flat and saw her on the other side. She obviously saw me and stopped to look in the window of a shop whose contents were unlikely to interest her, giving me time to catch up. I crossed and she turned, feigning surprise. From the waist down, I was like jelly. I was certain I could have turned the encounter into at least the promise of an affair but I didn't. After a few fumbling pleasantries I left her. Perhaps it was the old Hippocratic thing but I really think that I could not betray the trust with which, like a frightened animal, she allowed me to drive a needle into her, knowing I would be as gentle as I could.

Of course, refilling an A-P could cause trouble, one of the most feared of which was haemorrhage into the pleural cavity.

One night after dinner, I was called by Sister O'G to come

and see a young Irish girl who had been admitted that afternoon after a "difficult" refill. Maureen was sixteen, dark, pale, sweaty, and breathless. On percussing her chest, there was the dullness of liquid over half of the right side. An x-ray confirmed a "fluid level" and suggested there were about four pints of liquid in the chest. I put in a needle and drew out what looked like pure blood. I was prepared for this, however, and quickly estimated the haemoglobin concentration, which was thirty to forty per cent that of blood, indicating that she had not bled more than two pints into the chest and that the rest was tissue fluid exuded in response to the irritation of the blood. I suppose that today I would have given her a blood transfusion but even in general hospitals at that time blood transfusion was quite a performance, and at the Brompton it would take some time to organise. So I determined her blood group to be sure she would not be difficult to match with blood from one of us and set to work to get the blood out of her chest. There is really only one safe place for blood – inside blood vessels. When it escapes it is very irritating to the tissues and, particularly in places like the pleural cavity, it can cause an inflammation leading to thickening of the pleural lining and obliteration of the cavity. This was not only bad for the lung but made the care of the underlying TB much more difficult.

I sat Maureen up in her bed leaning forward over a pillow and the bed table and with Sister O'G's help (typical of her type and the times, she would not dream of going off duty and leaving things to the night nurse) I fairly quickly and easily removed thirty ounces of blood using a standard needle. It occasionally got blocked with little bits of clotted blood but I was able to clear these with a syringe of saline. But then I began to get air coming back into the syringe, and inserting the needle through the next two or three spaces lower down was not productive. I didn't get air but the flow was very spasmodic and I was unsure whether the needle was being blocked by blood clots or by the diaphragm. Maureen was quite breathless and her diaphragm was probably going up and down like a piston. I had no wish to go through the diaphragm and add a lacerated liver to the evening's problem, so I adopted a different approach. I brought up another bed and turned Maureen on her side with her right buttock on two pillows on her own bed and her shoulder on the other. In this way I hoped to get the blood to pool high up in her chest. I then got a divan from the day room and arranged some pillows on it for myself and positioned it between the two beds. I have always regarded it essential in the performance of technical procedures that the operator must be comfortable; otherwise the muscular ache of an uncomfortable position causes a subtle deterioration in technique – the needle loses its place. I then took up the position of a motor mechanic fixing a silencer and inserted a trochar and cannula. A cannula is much wider than a needle and a trochar goes down inside it to act as its cutting head. With the cannula I hoped to avoid blockage by the small blood clots and other debris I was sure were floating about in her chest. Well, it worked and another two pints came out over the next half hour or so.

Although the loss of blood was not extreme, Maureen was, not surprisingly, agitated. Sister O'G described her as "shocky", that is not in shock but on the edge of it, and in Sister O'G's book the treatment for shock was brandy. Throughout the entire drama, she kept administering sips of brandy interspersed with firm motherly Irish reassurance appropriate to one of her own kind. I suspected that behind my back Sister O'G also took a few sips herself but I was later told she was a strict teetotaller. At any rate as I was about to take up my position she said, "What about having a drop yourself Mr Campbell?" From then on the medicinal bottle passed freely between us. We did not consume much but what we consumed, together with our growing success, induced a euphoria which was most noticeable in Maureen. Perhaps lying down helped the circulation through her brain; at any rate she became not only cheerful but flattering and eventually amorous. "You're a marvellous docther"...and later "I love you." Maureen's trouble was on the right side but in her case I needed the help of gravity, so Maureen was gazing down at me over a nubile breast with what in daylight I later found were big, brown eyes. At one juncture she tried to kiss me and thereby nearly fell on top of me in the gap between the two beds. Despite the fact that the cannula was blunt I hastily withdrew it, not wishing to impale the lung or heart. Sister O'G, however, grabbed her with a "Hush, child, what do you think you're saying." Eventually I withdrew the cannula confident that I had got as much out as possible. The x-ray next morning showed only a small residue.

Of course Maureen had to stay in hospital for a few days and although she was not my patient, I had to visit her. She was subdued and a little shame-faced from the teasing of the other patients but there was no doubt that I had touched her heart – metaphorically at least.

In addition to bed rest and the A-P, several other means were used to close TB cavities and rest the lung. The phrenic nerve to the diaphragm was crushed to lessen the breathing on that side. Air was pumped into the belly to push the diaphragm up and collapse the lung. Surgeons removed the ribs to allow the chest to cave in. Some surgeons were even daring to cut out the diseased bits of the lungs (this being made much safer by a preliminary course of drugs). But within a few years this had all changed. Indeed, the writing was already on the wall; I was the first house physician who never induced (that is, started) an A-P for JGS – although I started several for GEB. The drugs took over and surgery was reserved for the removal of destroyed lungs. The last A-P clinic closed five years later and today even bed rest is used only for people who are feverish and severely ill with TB. In developing countries it has been shown that TB can be eliminated by outpatient treatment with drugs. Today the problem of TB in the West is confined to immigrants from those countries and to older people whose TB, acquired thirty or forty years ago, becomes "reactivated". They are a problem not so much to themselves as to the relatives and nurses they may infect.

The Traviatas and Mimis of today have leukaemia, not consumption. But in all conscience, neither of these is as nice and clean a way to go as their romantic images would have you believe.

Ultimately the most significant thing that happened to me

at the Brompton was non-medical. By tradition, the semifinals of the interhospitals nurses' tennis cup were played at the Brompton. For the nurses of the London teaching hospitals this competition was the equivalent of the rugger cup for the students. One Thursday during JGS's outpatient clinic, I popped across to the tennis court because Middlesex were playing Guys – the usual winners. When I got there, "our" second doubles pair were playing and I chatted with the first pair. One of these was pretty, dark, and vivacious. The other was goodlooking rather than pretty and she did not make an immediate impression but when their turn came to play, I was struck with her grace and power and intrigued by the gentle almost apologetic smile she gave her opponents as she swept them off the court. I decided to keep both of these girls in mind when I went back to the Middlesex.

No nonsense medicine

In the autumn of 1952, I passed the membership at the fourth attempt. My repeated failures were, at the time, demoralising but with hindsight I quite enjoyed the contests, particularly when face to face with the examiners in the clinical part. In my earlier attempts I had failed to realise that the membership is a higher examination in medicine and not an examination in higher medicine. Since the war it had ceased to be a test of fitness to be a consulting physician and had become a test of fitness to train to be one. The examiners wanted sound clinical competence and no nonsense. In the written and oral parts of the examination I tended to be too academic so that, although I always passed the clinical my total marks were too low. Even so, if one took a sporting view, and in those days the membership was regarded that way, my record wasn't bad: three "semifinals" (pathology vivas) and two "finals" (final vivas).

With the MRCP I was a respectable candidate for registrar jobs. By now I was really enjoying my work in the physiology department and would have liked another year there to complete the studies I saw stretching before me and to write my thesis. Because of a combination of circumstances, however, four out of five of the registrar jobs came up at the end of 1952. Sammy agreed I should apply and he would try to arrange that I could complete my PhD as a part-time student. One of these registrarships was to Dr HL Marriot. I had never worked for him but I knew that he had a good opinion of me. This opinion dated from 1946 when he had given the Croonion Lectures on salt and water metabolism. During the BSc year, I had been particularly interested in this topic and I wrote to him criticising his account on a number of points.

Only later did I realise what an extraordinary act of lèse majesté this letter might have seemed. Certainly I do not remember such a thing happening again in the fifteen years I spent at the Middlesex. He was not at all put out, however. Indeed he asked me to come and see him after I had qualified if I would like to do some research with him. By 1952 I had qualified but he had stopped doing research and I was working in another field; but I suppose I was a shoe-in for his job. I had some misgivings because as a clinician he was regarded as a bit of a joke: unable to elicit physical signs and prone to overinvestigation. In the event I came to have a very high regard for him.

He was a big muscular man who marched rather than walked. His head was of a shape which I believe resembled that of a Prussian officer. His visage was forbidding. I have never come across an expression as grim and unsmiling as the one he normally adopted. However, this expression did not reflect his temperament which was very jovial and hearty.

He was very concerned with practical matters and had a distaste for the niceties of diagnosis. He had shown this former characteristic before the war when he had, together with Alan Kekwick, pioneered practical blood transfusion. During the war in India, by the rational management of salt and water depletion, he had been responsible for a great reduction in the mortality from such illnesses as dysentery. His dislike of the one-upmanship of medicine was brought home to me when, as a student, I diagnosed a patient as having Behcet's syndrome; at that time almost unknown in Britain. When, bursting with pride, I suggested the diagnosis to him he asked me what could be done for it. When I told him that I didn't think anything could be done, he told me that that was a fat lot of use and stumped off without any word of praise.

At the start of his ward round I, as his registrar, had to hand him a foolscap sheet on which were four columns: the patient's name, the problem, the decisions taken on the last round, and a space for today's decisions. These he filled in and then took the sheet away with him. If the patient was to be discharged he insisted that the referring doctor receive a letter as soon as possible and preferably before the patient left hospital. He would decide if he or I was to write this letter. At the next round he would hand me copies of his letters and, if the patient was of particular interest to him, I had to give him a copy of mine. His letters were a model of clarity. All the usual constituents were there under subheadings but his recommendations were much more precise than I was used to and he employed two unusual but characteristic sections: "What the patient thinks" and "What I have told the patient".

Needless to say, his rounds were conducted with military precision, with the dignity of the patient (and of himself) paramount. They were also expeditious without being rushed. A tip he gave me when faced with a loquacious patient: "Draw up a chair and sit down. Much easier to get away if you don't seem to be in a hurry."

One of his stocks in trade was a steady supply of ex-officers from India and the East who had disturbances of the bowel or vague abdominal pain, or both. His main focus of interest in these patients was amoebiasis – to exclude it if possible and to treat it if suspected. He was also determined to take as little time as possible about these matters so he had evolved a sequence or programme of investigations designed to detect this and any other disorder of the bowel. Many of these patients were by now fairly important and this concern for their time was much appreciated. The routine began with a purgative which elicited "hot stools" to be rushed for microscopic examination for the dreaded amoeba. This purgation also emptied the bowel and facilitated x-ray examination of the large intestine by barium enema. And so it went on. HLM hated equivocation. If a radiologist reported something vague in the barium enema he would go and see the man and try to persuade him that what he saw was "just a turd".

Another feature of his approach to patients of this sort was his reluctance to keep them in hospital waiting for the results of investigation or of treatment. If the patient was discharged for readmission when the results of investigations were to hand or when he needed reassessment of the effects of treatment the doctor would be sent an interim letter to keep him informed. HLM would often make use of this letter as a programme for what was to be done at the subsequent admission. Once he gave me copies of letters about two such patients. I gave them to a secretary to put in the patients' case records but when the patients were readmitted the letters were not there. Although I had only been in the job a couple of months, I realised I was in trouble which I thought to head off as we chatted en route from the consultants' dining room to the ward. At such times HLM was jovial and seemed to be approachable.

"Sir, when they were discharged, you gave me letters about Mr X and Brigadier Y."

"Campbell, I take it you are trying to tell me that these letters are lost. If this happens again, I'll have your appointment reviewed at the next opportunity."

Clearly, he was going to stand no nonsense.

Needless to say, from then on I was on tenterhooks whenever he was around but I enjoyed working for him and I served him well. Before one of our last rounds I had to tell him about a difficult patient and a complicated professional situation and how I had handled them during the preceding weekend. The problem involved if and when to operate and I wanted him to decide if he wanted to take over or leave me to carry on. Either way he ought to be properly informed. I embarked, therefore, on a fairly detailed summary. He stood looking at me steadily, his eyes never leaving mine, his features grave and motionless. After two or three minutes, he broke in.

"Campbell, do I look as though I am listening?"

"Yes."

"In private practice, it's a useful trick."

"But you understand the position?"

"Of course." Small smile. "Carry on." Quiet chuckle. "I've every confidence." Suppressed guffaw.

A feest of love diseeses

At the hospital skins and VD went together. The same consultant was in charge of both and his registrar spent most of his time in skin clinics and lived in outer London. From the medical standpoint this arrangement was acceptable because neither skins nor VD present dramatic emergencies at odd times. There was need, however, for "cover" for patients coming after hours to the discreetly labelled "special clinic" which was always open near the casualty department. It fell to my lot in 1953 to become the registrar responsible for "back up" for this clinic and also to do the weekly evening follow up clinic for syphilis which was too inconvenient for the proper registrar whose main interests were in skins and who, as I say, lived in the outer suburbs. The whole operation depended upon Mr Johnson. Mr J was straight out of Wodehouse. He played Jeeves to my Bertie, if you'll allow that my scruffy pad in St Pancras was not up to Bertie's life style. In saying that, I am merely conveying the role Mr J adopted and the station in life I was thereby made to play up to. He treated me as the senior petty officer in a crack ship treats the wettest, new midshipman: and he was difficult to live up to. His stiff white collar and shiny black shoes contrasted with my curled, yellowing Aertex shirt and battered brothel creepers. Also he ran a post-war Rover while I could only afford to share a 1934 Morris 10. How did he manage a Rover? It was rumoured that certain clients were persuaded that he could clear up their problems more quickly from a private source of imported American penicillin than with the NHS stuff.

Mr J was a registered nurse. He had been a sickbay attendant in the Royal Navy during the war and his whole demeanour was a combination of senior petty officer and gentleman's gentleman. He was impeccably groomed and came to work with a rolled umbrella. He even managed to make the hospital's patched white coats look like a uniform worthy of the ward room. He always stood up in my presence and called me "Sir". Of course he knew far more about veneral diseases than I did but even when we came to know each other very well he would always give me advice by saying with a little cough, "Sir, I thought that we might consider another touch of penicillin."

We were answerable to two consultants. For most official purposes and most patients Dr Ray Bettley, the dermatologist, was boss but for the hard core of cases with long standing syphilis of the nervous system we had to be careful of Mac, the senior neurologist. Dr Bettley was popular with the students and was once "taken off" at the Christmas concert as "the white rabbit". He always wore a silver tie and his shoulders were covered with more dandruff than one would expect of a man in his line of business. Certainly Mr J's hair was better looked after than his. Of course Mr J always gave him his proper name but after that Chirstmas concert I used affectionately to refer to him as "the rabbit". The understanding between Mr J and myself was by this time such that he would not interpret this as a sign of disrespect. The attitudes of the rabbit and Mac to VD were very different. The rabbit had taken his postgraduate training in Paris and one of my predecessors in the job told me that in order to assure the ladies in Paris of their confidence in the efficacy of their treatment, the postgraduates there would be quite willing to accept a free sample of the ladies' favours – a sort of follow up!

Mac was quite different. I remember a poor Cypriot (who had had enough arsenic pumped into his veins and enough bismuth stuck in his backside to kill all the fish in a small lake but whose blood tests were still positive) asking with pathetic embarrassment through the medium of a nephew whether it was alright to "have relations" with his wife. Mac, the Calvinist, said to Mr J without looking at either, "Never. Has he never heard of the wages of sin?"

Most of Mr J's custom was of the sort you might expect: inhabitants of Soho with mild doses of the clap and he always seemed to have plenty of sailors. Perhaps his reputation was spread among the cafés of dockland. It was from him I first heard the story of the padre who went to the sick bay on one of His Majesty's ships in Port Said and showed the medical officer his urethral discharge. The MO pondered it silently, not because he had any doubt about the diagnosis but because he was not quite sure how to handle the social aspects. To break the silence the patient nervously suggested that perhaps it had caught cold while he was swimming. With a sigh the MO looked at his watch and said, "Well, let's give it a minute. If it hasn't sneezed in that time, I'm afraid I'm going to have to call it clap."

Once syphilis has got into the system the bug can no longer be found and one relies on indirect tests. In my time the test was the WR or Wasserman Reaction. Like all indirect tests it is occasionally liable to give either false positive or false negative results. The trouble with the WR was that it gave too many false positives. The WR is an immunological test and like so much of immunology, the making of the ingredients leaves room for skills which are closer to those of the cook than the scientist. I never met the person who did the cooking at the hospital but I came to think she was probably an embittered old spinster. Certainly it wasn't safe to have your WR done while you were even having a wicked thought if she was doing the test, and this was not always funny. When I was responsible for the medical care of the antenatal clinic I had a lot of trouble handling patients whose routine screening WR was reported as positive. I fear that the marriages of several young couples were put under some strain by the findings. When I was a casualty officer, before I had responsibility for the VD clinic, a pathetic retired civil servant whose prostate was beginning to affect his behaviour came to see me one busy Monday morning having had it off with one of the whores on Saturday night. I told him that there was no way that I could give him complete reassurance for several weeks but he insisted on coming back every few days and asking for a blood test. It came back positive. The result may have been a false positive or it may have been the relic of some long past indescretion but it was certainly not due to his brief encounter in Greek Street. I had to send him to the VD clinic, however, and a few days later I heard that he had killed himself.

In the two years during which I was heavily involved and in subsequent years when I occasionally "stood in" I only saw five really genuine "primary chancres" – that is fresh new cases of recently acquired syphilis. All of these were acquired outside Britain. One afternoon in the middle of a busy clinic, Mr J rang me. "I think you'd like to come down if you don't mind Sir. I think we have a real one. If you're too busy I can certainly get things under way but I really do think you'd like to see it or" – and there was a little chuckle – "them." Consultations with Mr J never took very long so between clinic patients I dashed over to his little room where I found a short, swarthy man of Levantine appearance (a sailor, of course) lying on the couch with his private parts delicately covered with a starched white towel. Mr J had more of a grin than he usually permitted himself and he handed me a scrappy piece of paper which he was holding by the extreme corner between his finger and his thumb in a way that indicated his distate. On this scrap of paper was written: "Plees see my frend he has a feest of love diseeses." When I looked at Mr J he permitted himself a chuckle and said, "I think he's right Sir."

As I was pondering this request for a consultation, Mr J said: "Mat'lot of course, Sir." And then after a disdainful glance, "Probably deck'and on a tramp."

"Shall we look a little closer Sir?" he said, offering me a pair of powdered gloves on another crisply laundered towel. When I had donned these he peeled back the top layer of the towel to reveal a pretty athletic looking penis. The shaft was even more bronzed than its weather beaten owner but I suspect owed its healthy tan to friction rather than the wind or the ultraviolet. Mr J had of course cleaned up the immediate neighbourhood but the surrounding grime suggested that the parts had infrequent contact with either light or water. Altogether, it was definitely a beast of nocturnal habits. On one side the foreskin was slightly reddened and swollen so that the wrinkles were smoothed out and there was a little thin discharge creeping out from under it. On drawing it back I found three raised, firm red spots, one of which had ulcerated.

Having assumed that the patient spoke no English I said, "What a beauty. I must get some students to see this." Then, I am ashamed to say for an hour or so there was a steady stream of students pretending to be doctors. Typical cases of anything are rare so that one always tried to show them to the students. A typical case of something by this time really rare but which continued to be described in text books and asked about in "finals" was particularly valuable teaching material that the students ought to see. Today I suppose I would have to say that I was anxious to share this learning experience with the students.

Every time you looked at his face – and this was something the students only did out of curiosity and with embarrassment – he gave a rather sheepish grin. At first I thought this was shame but when I came back from the clinic to see what the smear taken from the chancre showed under the microscope, the sheepish grin had turned into something rather self confident and now it was definitely quite proud. The slide itself was also in its own way a pleasure to look at. There were lots of twitching little corkscrews. His WR was positive, which it really shouldn't have been if this was the first time he had had syphilis, but then as Mr J said, "You can't really be surprised with that sort of mat'lot."

I had little hope that we could give him the standard course of penicillin with all of the follow up visits the text books recommended, so Mr J and I agreed to give him a couple of massive doses of penicillin and hope that he would come back. He never did but two weeks later the night nurse gave Mr J a box of evil cigars which she said a small dark man had by sign language, late the previous night, indicated were to be given to somebody in the little room. Mr J of course offered them to me, because I was the "officer in charge", but he knew I'd let him have them.

Hunting the huntress

I must have first seen Diana in the autumn of 1951 when I lectured her class or "set", as a cohort of trainee nurses was called, but I have no recollection of her until that Thursday afternoon at the Brompton (see *No More Mimis*). I have a vivid memory of her appearance that afternoon. She had – and has – a handsome face which is beautiful square on but which, in profile, is slightly spoiled for cover girl use by a bump on the nose and a strong jaw. These heavy features she did not help by wearing her hair in a row of curls around the bottom at ear length. She is really striking with her hair piled up and forward. At that time she was also rather big — not fat, just muscular. When brother Brian first met her he said, "Who's Muscles? You want to be careful of her, she'll kill you!" She has a lovely, gentle smile and her eyes dance when she laughs. A year or so after we first met she shed many pounds and revealed a gorgeous figure. But she was most truly beautiful in movement. On the tennis court she had a lazy power which always attracted spectators. She had been the number one player at the unfashionable Chelmsford High School, which had beaten all the cream of the nation's girls' schools to win the all-England championship (the Aberdare Cup) at Wimbledon. Even when we met, with no coaching and several years past her prime, she took four days off from night duty to play in the West of England tournament at Torquay. She was beaten in the first round by the eventual winner, a Wightman cup player, but not before Diana took a set from her. Her tennis will always bring up the unspoken question of what might have been had she concentrated on it rather than nursing. I have it on good opinion that she would have been a Wimbledon player of international calibre but I don't think that she would have gone to the top simply because she lacks the killer instinct. Tennis was never as important as nursing and is never as important as the home and family. Even so, in her fifties, Diana was the most sought after player in the local club tournaments and was generally accepted as the best player in the city – even though she was occasionally beaten by other more determined ladies.

She does everything at speed, even sewing or knitting. I am not well coordinated and it is a continuous pleasure for me to watch her doing things better than I can. She inherits these attributes from her mother. From her father she gets over-weening modesty, gentleness, and monumental common sense. From neither parent has she acquired the gift of the gab.

At the beginning of 1953, I and several of my contemporaries became registrars and Diana was one of a group of senior nurses who together with us formed a loose social group from which several marriages emerged. For a couple of years, however, the link between us all had no strong sexual or romantic overtones. We worked together, went to the local pub after duty, had numerous parties in the residency, played tennis and squash, and went to the theatre (usually on free passes sent to the nurses' home by poorly attended shows.)

She has since told me that she had a crush on me for a few weeks shortly after we met. I was unaware of this and the affliction passed. Through 1953 and the first half of 1954, I had a busy love life with usually two glamour pusses on the go at once and several "bits on the side", but Diana was growing on me. I remember the first time I knew I was in trouble. We had arranged to play squash one evening after she came off duty. I arrived first and was knocking the ball about in the forecourt when I heard the door close. I turned and saw her standing there, very erect as she smoothed her shirt down into her skirt. She was all brown, lithe, white, and smiling.

With the example of my parents' poor marriage in mind I fought against Diana but hedged my bets by getting her to let me go to her home to see her on her own turf. She was reluctant to do this, so one afternoon when she was on nights off we ostensibly set off to go to Cambridge but I took a "wrong" turning to the east near Epping and went hither and thither ever eastward on country roads until Diana had to admit we were near her home at Writtle. "Well, let's go and have a surprise tea at your home." She agreed unenthusiastically. I still don't know why. She cannot have been ashamed of the family home, Writtle Mead, because it was a friendly, rambling, mock Jacobean house with a large garden, grass tennis court, and apple orchards. Only sister Margaret was at home and although she was not at all put out by our appearance, I was conscious of surreptitious sidelong glances.

I was impressed with the look and feel of her home and was pleased when a few weeks later she asked me there for the weekend. In my conceit I thought my emergent feelings were eliciting a response so I determined to be on my guard. I was wrong.

On the Sunday afternoon we went for a walk across the fields. She wore a white, strapless, Horrocks dress with a small pattern of oranges and lemons and a full skirt. As she went ahead of me and swung lazily over a stile, I knew I was lost. That evening, as we were getting ready to leave, she lay down on her bed waiting for me. I walked in carrying my holdall, stooped down, kissed her and said the usual three words for the first time in my life. She looked puzzled and said nothing. Embarrassed, I walked out of the room and back in again; still she said nothing and now she looked slightly worried.

In silence we drove off in my little Morris and still said nothing for twenty minutes, all the way to Ongar. There is a sharp, right hand turn in Ongar and I set myself the deadline of breaking the ice before we reached it. I don't know what I said but the gist was that, if she loved me as I loved her, we should get married and she should come to Baltimore with me rather than do her midwifery and possibly become an air stewardess as she had planned.

We went back to the flat and she lay on the bed while I sat

on the floor beside her and tried to persuade her to sleep with me. She quietly but firmly refused and made it clear that her refusal had nothing to do with love. As Ford Maddox Ford wrote, "some do not". It was only after a few days that I realized that my whole approach was based on the misconception that she returned my love: she did not.

The next three weeks or so are blurred. I came to realise that she was fond of me but my reputation as a philanderer stood in the way. I also remember twinges of doubt on my side. One evening I took her to the theatre. She had obviously sought to dress to kill but the effect was not what she had intended; she switched me off. Her hair was in tight curls and the dress was a nondescript blue and shapeless. It neither clothed her breasts nor showed them. The waist was down around her hips and the skirt was neither long nor short. And her shoes were neither high nor low heeled.

Throughout these weeks my love and conceit, helped by her gentleness, never wavered in their belief that she would fall and I made no further attempt to seduce her. As a private gesture, I broke off my other affairs. Then one morning, with obvious difficulty, Diana told me that she had come to love me. As far as I remember I made no natural response such as proposing to her. I had a long standing pact with myself that I would never propose when the blood was hot. She had met Mother, who obviously liked her, so I next took her to Yorkshire to meet Pa. She stayed with Mrs P, Pa's girlfriend, and I stayed with Pa. We went for drives and walks but the conversation was stilted and Pa did not mention her. In fact he didn't seem to take much notice of her.

On the last morning, however, circumstances were propitious. It was drizzling and Diana was still in bed when I went to Mrs P's to collect her. I went into the bedroom and found her all tousled and without any make up. So I sat on the side of the bed and asked her to marry me. She nodded and kissed me.

I said nothing to Pa but wrote to him when we got back to London, warning him that our engagement would be announced in the paper within the next few days. To my surprise he phoned me. "That's all right" he said, "she's a sensible

The author's father, Dr E. Gordon Campbell

School sportsday 1935

The author's marriage to Diana, 18 December 1954

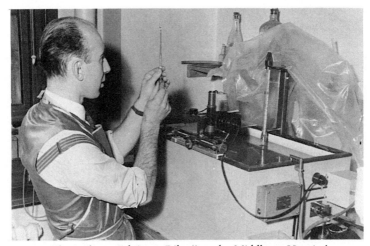

The author – "doing a Riley" at the Middlesex Hospital

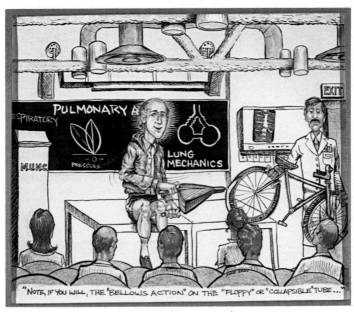

An interesting lecturing technique

girl and she has capable hands. There's much more to her than the last two awful creatures of yours I've met."

Diana told her parents and I received a rather gushing letter from her mother: "So happy that you have decided to share life's journey..." Then the planning took over; it had to be hurried because in three months we had to go to the States which meant setting up a sequence of procedures to get Diana's visa as soon as we produced a marriage certificate.

The scene became clouded about six weeks before the wedding when, out of the blue, I developed a severe and inexplicable inflammatory iritis in my right eye. Now iritis is often the first sign of some unpleasant general disease – including clap and the pox – so I nervously suggested to Diana that we should call a halt to the plans. Quietly and gently she dismissed the suggestion. She had made her decision for better or for worse and if the worse happened to precede the technicality of the wedding – so what?

So, on 18th December, 1954, we had a village wedding and a joyous reception in a large marquee in the garden. It was a beautiful midwinter's day with a gentle sun. Brian did me well as best man; Diana was lovely in the dress she had made herself and the bridesmaids were pretty in primrose dresses she had designed.

We spent the first night at the Berkeley in Mayfair (outrageously extravagant) and then spent four nights touring in the old Morris in the Cotswolds, staying two nights in the Bay Tree at Burford where, to our horror, they initially showed us a bedroom with twin beds. On getting the message, however, they changed us to the most romantic room in the inn.

We went back to Diana's home for Christmas and then took the *Queen Elizabeth* to New York, doing our best in the single berths of a tourist cabin on R deck. We spent a couple of nights in New York and then took the train to Baltimore to a surprised Dick and Polly who had never realised where this wife had come from. I was single when I had sent Dick my application and had never told him formally about my change of status. Polly put us in their twin bedded, spare room for our first night in that house, which was to be the scene of so many happy memories, the first of which was the sight of an overwhelming Matisse over the fireplace. They were tickled to find that we used only one small bed.

Then we walked the streets until we found a ground floor flat at 1923 McElderry St where the married house staff still hung out, within walking distance of the hospital, and in what was otherwise an all-black and violent neighbourhood. Diana found a job in the premature baby unit in Harriet Lane. I worked (see *Bloody Gases*). We drank California sherry and ate liver and bacon, bought an old Plymouth and tried to live on $100.00 a month. Fortunately Diana was allowed to go on working month by month, which brought in an extra $250.00.

We fought the cockroaches, suffered the heat, and we were very happy.

Bloody gases

For the first two or three weeks in January 1955 I was ill at ease in the lab at Johns Hopkins. I was a new boy and a foreigner to boot but beneath these surface problems was an angst, a compound of anxiety, guilt, and fear. I thought I was a fraud: I did not think I could hack it as a real scientist. Why should I think so? After all I had completed a PhD and defended it successfully, had papers published in the prestigious and rigorous *Journal of Physiology*, and so on. I had not yet come to realise, however, that the world of science is a world of ideas. I still dumbly regarded it as a world of knowledge and of technique in which the good research workers were distinguished from dilettantes like me by their knowledge of physics and chemistry, their mathematical skill, and, above all, by their manual dexterity with laboratory equipment. In none of these had I any confidence or accomplishments.

Between the ages of fifteen and seventeen I had learned physics, chemistry, and biology; chiefly at night school and not for their own sakes but in order to pass the first MB exam. Furthermore, the first time I took the exam, I failed. My ability to use mathematics was weak. For one happy year before school certificate I was stimulated by a teacher who encouraged an interest in the concepts and implications of maths but before and after him I had been ground into accepting that I was no more than a good, average student because I never got all the sums right. Above all I had a nagging, sickening sense of technical incompetence which had begun during the cramming to pass the first MB. Although I usually made the experiments in physics work, I had trouble with chemistry and biology was a disaster. I wrecked everything I touched. After one hopelessly destructive attempt to dissect the nerves of the head of a frog, the teacher said she hoped I had no intention of becoming a surgeon or at least to warn her if I intended to practice in her part of the world. My cackhandedness with scalpel, scissors, and forceps was embarrassing but ironically, few surgical operations are as demanding as the nerves of the head of a frog.

My self deprecation was reinforced in the early years at medical school. In the year and a half we spent dissecting a human body my colleagues rarely allowed me to use a scalpel. In the physiology laboratory I was allowed – indeed encouraged – only to design and direct experiments but never to perform them; never to operate on the animal or analyse the blood samples. This pattern continued even during the PhD years. The basic tool I had used in my research, the electromyograph, detects muscular contractions but it does not really measure them and the instrument required no great skill to drive. It often went wrong and then I was totally dependent on the technician, an ex-RAF radar operator. I tried to rectify some of these deficiencies by taking a night school course in electronics and reading *Calculus Made Easy* and other books on mathematics for scientists but the self doubt remained. I thought my PhD was a reasonably competent piece of descriptive, functional anatomy but not really scientific, and now came the time of truth.

In my application for the research fellowship I had said I wanted to learn Riley's method for blood gas measurement and his method for analysing gas exchange defects in the lungs; yet I doubted my manual skill to do the one or my mathematical skill to do the other. Now I was out on a limb. In the early days in the lab no particular reference was made to these matters. The methods were being used all the time and the tradition seemed to be for the fellows to use their own initiative in picking up the requisite skills. I learned how to put the Riley needle into an artery because the fellows took it in turns to take the arterial bloods on the wards but nobody pressed me to do the analysis. I also turned taps on collection bags during some of the big studies on oxygen uptake during exercise — but again I was able to avoid exposing my incompetence.

When someone new joins a research group there is often a period of embarrassment and indecision about what he is going to do and with whom. This embarrassment is particularly likely if the new man is paid for by a fellowship or scholarship and is not therefore an employee for whom the boss will have specific tasks. Sometimes the new boy will have very clear ideas about what he wants to do and sometimes the boss has things he wants doing and suggests, advises, or even directs accordingly. Commonly, however, an uncomfortable ritual takes place which is akin to a proposal of marriage – or at any rate an offer of seduction. The new boy has friendly but inconclusive talks with several of the members of the department. He is too shy to say he would like to work on their projects in case he should seem to be muscling in. They are too shy to invite him to join them because they doubt he is really interested. Very occasionally there is substance in the fear of the new boy being thought a free loader or in the fear of the host worker that his ideas may be stolen or his glory diminished. I do not think these are often the real causes of the difficulty in getting a new boy started. I think the true difficulty lies in the very personal nature of scientific research. The really creative part of science is having ideas and the examination of these arguments can be very emotional, particularly when they are just beyond the edge of clarity: intuitively felt but ineffable. Given the ideas then examination by experiment, "the demanding but lesser occupation" as Sir Peter Medawar rightly calls it, still leaves room for idiosyncracy. The choice of type of experiment; how to do it; when, how often, and what to measure, can all be shared excitements or causes of disagreement, or worse.

In later years I would ask a new boy joining our group if he had any ideas he wanted to work on and gave him a superficial account of who was doing what and then leave him to mooch around for two or three weeks, in the romantic belief that the scientist loves to work on his own ideas. If no alliance formed, I then pushed the newcomer into a project and into the arms of one of the others in the lab (including myself). Usually this arranged marriage was welcomed by both parties whose shyness had prevented either of them making the necessary pass.

So it was in the lab at Hopkins. For a week or so I wandered aimlessly round watching apprehensively as the technicians analysed the oxygen and carbon dioxide in gas and blood samples with breathtaking speed and accuracy while chatting casually in Baltimorean drawls. In the meantime I made ineffectual attempts to work the electronic equipment used for measuring the pressure flows and volume of air.

In fairness my awkwardness in the lab was due to more than my real or perceived incompetence. The equipment was strange, more advanced and occasionally totally new compared with that in a British lab of the time. To try and alleviate my angst I asked slow, gentle, young Fritzy, the technician, to take me through the use of one of the simpler gas analysers. She quickly showed me and then left me to fly it solo. I had to go back to her so often with questions and made such a mess of the instrument that eventually she sat by me and watched me go through the analysis step by step. Her big brown eyes hinted that she couldn't decide if I was clumsy, stupid, or just British.

The basic processes of respiration are simple. The act of breathing pumps fresh air into the lungs; the blood takes up oxygen and gives off carbon dioxide; and the air breathed out is altered accordingly. Because the essential processes are simple, however, and the various pressures and concentrations can be measured, the workings of respiration have been treated with a rigour unsurpassed by any other bodily process. This mathematical rigor was essentially a product of the Second World War. Before the war there was a sound, qualitative grasp of respiratory physiology and a few leaders had hinted at quantitative treatments. The real push to become precise came from the need to be able to fly higher than the enemy, which meant getting oxygen into the blood even when the barometric pressure was very low. This need focussed physiologists and engineers on the need to describe the workings of respiration with precision. Joe Lilienthal, the head of the lab, and Dick Riley, my new boss at Hopkins, had been part of this endeavour in the US Naval Air Service. They had developed a theoretical analysis of the processes governing the uptake of oxygen in the lungs and had developed a method for measuring the pressure of the oxygen and carbon dioxide in the blood – the notorious bubble method to which I will return later.

The theoretical analysis of the oxygen uptake in the lungs depended upon the use of certain equations. One did not have to understand the origin or derivation of these equations to apply the analysis but I suspected it was only right and proper that one should. Furthermore, I had been told that all competent American respiratory research workers took these equations in their stride. So after lunch one day I asked Leon Farhi, an Israeli fellow somewhat senior to me but with whom I felt less embarrassed in my ignorance, if he could derive them. "Sure", he said and offered to show me then and there. Two hours and umpteen sheets of paper later I agreed that, while he had not been able to derive any of the equations, he had given me a good idea of the principles underlying them. With an impish grin Leon told me he had once been able to derive them and could probably do so again if I really wanted to know how. I was relieved that this clever chap found the equations difficult but I regret to say I did not get the real message – to understand these tools sufficiently to use them does not mean one has to be able to recapitulate their derivation.

I became involved in two projects. The second in command of the lab, Dick Shepard, tentatively suggested we might examine what happens to the size of the bronchial tubes during deep breathing using the mass spectrometer, a remarkable instrument which measures many gases instantaneously and simultaneously. Dick's approach had been tentative because he did not think I would be interested but I leapt at the offer. Fortunately our plans required me to be a subject for the experiments (which required a lot of disciplined breathing), so I did not have to operate the mass spectrometer and my technical incompetence was again hidden. In the second study I worked with Harry Martin, one of the American fellows, on the mechanisms which govern how fast you can breathe out and what obstucts the air flow in asthma and emphysema. These experiments required the measurement of pressure in the chest, which we obtained by swallowing balloons into the oesophagus (gullet). These balloons were much more delicate than the FLs I had used for studying stomach pressure but then the recording equipment at Hopkins was much better. In fact it was quite easy to use. We obtained promising results but had trouble on two counts. Firstly the changes we were studying were very rapid, just about at the limit of the ability of the equipment to respond. Secondly although we had a strong intuition or hunch about the problem, we did not have a satisfactory, rigorous model to use in interpreting our results and in predicting what should happen in other circumstances.

By this time life had settled into a rhythm. Diana and I had a ground floor apartment (which even Americans would call a flat) in McElderry Street, a hundred yards from Hopkins. Diana's job in the premature baby unit meant that she was usually on the 3 pm to midnight shift with an hour off between 5 and 6 pm. Work in the lab stopped about 5 pm so we were able to eat together. To save money, we ate at the flat rather than the hospital canteen. Then from 6 pm to midnight I usually worked in the lab, partly for convenience and, particularly when summer came, partly because the lab was air conditioned. Initially, I spent a lot of time trying to correct my failings. I read and reread the previous papers and books on the subjects under study in the lab. I practiced on the machines – but only the simple ones that could be mended by Fritzy. I even did yet another *Teach Yourself Mathematics* course for scientists.

As the weeks passed and our experiments began to show results, these evening hours were turned over to working out the results and trying to interpret them by drawing innumerable graphs. Every few days, whenever he was free or we had something new to discuss with him, we would have noisy discussions with Dick. Only when I was leaving did I appreciate the right way to use these occasions. I made the mistake of approaching each session expecting conclusions and plans for further experiments, But no. It was not always easy to get Dick to pay attention; he tried but his mind kept wandering and he would miss steps in the arguments or, if he did understand something and liked it, he would go off at a tangent. But his delayed action was superb. Get enough of the ideas across, give him some results and a few graphs, and he would come back next day or after the weekend with fresh ideas. Sometimes he went too far too fast. Once he presented me with a very wide ranging and precise graphical analysis of the pressures and flows in various parts of the airways and lungs using our findings. I protested that our equipment was not good enough for us to trust the data he had built into his edifice but he was so excited that he swept that quibble aside and went on explaining the merit of looking at things his way. I interrupted him with a pompous remark I have never regretted, "I was not brought up to speculate wildly on the basis of very few experimental facts obtained with equipment of questionable accuracy."

"Then you've come to the wrong place. I've spent my life doing just that."

The other, romantic and truer voice of science was speaking.

About two months after I joined the lab, Dick called me into his office. He hesitantly expressed pleasure that I was involved in two projects but pointed out that these had very little to do with his special interest, the blood gases. The value of his techniques and ideas was the major reason I had given for wishing to work with him. I had thought they could help me to sort out the way to treat respiratory failure. He went on to point out that, other than himself, there was now no one in the lab who could do the bubble method. Two fellows who had mastered it had left and the best analytical technician had been spirited away to Canada by another fellow who sensibly decided that this approach to the bubble was easier than learning it. Fritzy, although she knew how to do the bubble, could not get consistent results. Much of the continuing work in the lab needed blood gas measurements and Dick, with his other commitments, was not always available.

I got the drift and my heart sank. The bubble method was

notoriously difficult. How could I, who could not dissect the nerves of the frog or fill a test tube without breaking it, possibly master the bubble? I attempted to demur but Dick quite rightly pointed out that I had no option unless I wanted to renege on my fellowship.

It was agreed, therefore, that I would retire to the back lab with the spare set of equipment for the bubble method. Fritzy would show me the steps and when I had the hang of it Dick would coach me.

Why all this fuss? Surely it's easy to measure oxygen and carbon dioxide in blood. True, it is not difficult to measure the amounts of these gases in the blood but for many purposes one wants to know their presssures. The chemical arrangements are complex: oxygen is attached to haemoglobin and carbon dioxide is in the form of bicarbonate, so the relation of concentration (amount) to pressure (physical activity) is variable. Today measurements of oxygen and carbon dioxide pressures in blood are routine in all hospitals but in the late 'forties and 'fifties, the bubble method was alone. The apparatus was simple; it consisted of a small one ml syringe onto which, where the needle would normally be, was attached a very fine bore, narrow glass capillary tube, ten cm long. The syringe was filled with blood to be analyzed and a small bubble of air was added. The syringe was then gently rotated in water at body temperature to allow the pressure of oxygen and carbon dioxide in the bubble to equilibrate with those in the blood. Next the syringe was pointed upwards and the bubble pushed up into the glass capillary. The length of the bubble was measured and then carbon dioxide and oxygen were selectively absorbed in succession by drawing suitable solutions down the capillary over the bubble and then pushing the bubble back up. The changes in volume of the bubble when carbon dioxide and oxygen were removed were proportional to their concentrations and hence to their pressures because, unlike the blood, there were no other confusing forms of oxygen and carbon dioxide.

The method was not really very complicated so why had it gained such a fearsome reputation? The trouble was in the manipulation of the bubble. The bubble had to be pushed gently and steadily along the fine capillary tube so that there was a smooth even surface without irregular blobs of blood or, the greatest dread, breaking the bubble. Two syringes of blood were used to obtain duplicate analysis. One was measured while the other was equilibrating. When on form with good syringes (these varied unpredictably: some were too stiff, some were loose, and some varied up and down the barrel) an analysis could be done in forty five minutes or so. But the procedure was so finicky that one was pretty pooped and for accurate work it was considered undesirable to do more than two or three bloods a day. (This was a rule I had to ignore completely when I returned to the study of patients in London.)

Surprise, surprise! I mastered the bubble and soon became Dick's stand in, even for quite important performances. The other Dick (Dick S) often tried to persuade the boss to calibrate the bubble method so that we would really know its accuracy and eventually, with the aid of a statistician, we embarked on a study designed to measure not only the overall accuracy of the method but also the importance of several of the key steps. The study required Dick and myself to analyse specially prepared blood samples with oxygen and carbon dioxide pressures known to our colleagues but not to us. We worked in separate labs and did not reveal our findings to each other until both had finished the analysis. We then swore on the lab book that the "run" (analysis) had been technically satisfactory and the results were to be accepted. There was to be no going back if the results were not nice, nor were results to be accepted because they were nice if the analyst was unhappy with his technique. All these rules were agreed to avoid bias – unconscious cheating. Dick didn't like them because they reduced the room in which he could use his "judgement". He had such habits as rejecting one of his pair of syringes if he didn't like the look of the bubble or weighting the average of the two results in favour of the syringe which was working better.

I, on the other hand, thought this study really was my

coming of age. It had everything: collaboration with the very best, a difficult method, a rigorous experimental design, and fancy statistics.

The study went well and was eventually published in a paper showing how the careful experimental design had enabled us to learn far more about the method from twenty experiments than had been learned from the hundreds published previously. But making the measurements was really rather a miserable experience. The prospect of doing a bubble was bad enough at any time and the realisation that each of these was to be part of the authoritative calibration could only increase the apprehension.

One Wednesday we did a run in the morning and then most of us in the lab went to Washington to the National Institutes of Health to discuss our work with one of the top men in the world on lung mechanics. When we returned we did another run. When finished, we met and agreed that the runs had been technically satisfactory and should be accepted. I worked out my results first and found the oxygen was rather high. Of course I did not know what the true oxygen reading was, but the value I had was odd. I went to see Dick who had been called away before working his results out. He agreed that the oxygen was a bit odd but, "that's the way it goes; sometimes you're just unlucky; looks as though your middle reading must have been long but I guess we'll have to stick by the rules."

Then he worked his results out and his oxygen values were even higher than mine. He said we must reject them and exclude both our results from the study. Again I got stuffy. "You cannot go around rejecting results just because you don't like them. A few minutes ago; you accepted mine as just bad luck."

We had another of our rare altercations, ended by Dick: "I don't care about these statisticians; these results are obviously nonsense and I won't be party to a study that includes them."

So we set the rules aside and did another run which produced more credible values.

Almost a week later we learned that while we were in

Washington, somebody from another lab had borrowed the valve from the air cylinder we used to put the bubbles in our syringes. He had used it for a cylinder of pure oxygen. He had put the valve back on our special cylinder but had not flushed it through so there were traces of pure oxygen in it when on Wednesday evening, thinking everything was as we had left it in the morning, we filled our syringes. Dick had filled his first and his syringes had therefore received bubbles with very high oxygen. I sometimes wonder what we would have done if I had filled my syringes before him!

The months passed. I acquired a sound grasp of most of respiratory physiology and three of our studies were published. In June I received a peremptory offer of a job at the Middlesex provided I returned in September. This cut my time well short of the year I had expected and as we were enjoying ourselves we were both disappointed. Jobs in academic medicine in Britain were very scarce, however, so needs must.

Diana and I did the statutory trip round the States and Canada in the old Plymouth, sleeping in a pup tent in the great campgrounds – thirty states, three provinces, cost three hundred dollars. And then back on the *Queen Mary*.

Respiratory failure in the 'fifties

Before 1950 respiratory failure as we know it today was scarcely recognised. Barcroft, Haldane, Henderson, and others had provided sound frameworks for understanding anoxia (lack of oxygen supply to the tissues), respiratory acidosis (excess retention of carbon dioxide), and the functional disorders which caused them. These topics were part of the undergraduate physiology curriculum which in my case had extra emphasis during a BSc year. None of this theoretical framework, however, was put to use in the wards.

These reflections are particularly concerned with respiratory failure in chronic lung disease and my memory of the story we learned as students (helped by reference to a few popular medical texts of the time) is as follows. People who suffer repeated attacks of acute (infective) bronchitis develop persistently infected bronchi. This condition is called chronic bronchitis and it leads on to destruction of the lungs, causing emphysema – which is manifested by breathlessness. Emphysema puts a strain on the right heart which eventually fails and causes cor pulmonale with oedema (abnormally large amounts of fluid in the tissues). Throughout this natural history the patient is liable to attacks of secondary infection during which he becomes anoxic. After the development of emphysema, the prognosis is poor and once cor pulmonale has developed, it is grave.

Not much notice was taken of these patients in London teaching hospitals. Neither the junior nor the senior staff

Published in a shortened version in the *British Medical Journal* 1979; ii: 657–8.

regarded them as "interesting" and their treatment was unrewarding. The chest physicians of the time were nearly all specialists in tuberculosis, which was naturally and correctly seen as a much more pressing problem. Blood gas measurements were so impractical as to be non-existent and oxygen therapy was clumsy and unpredictable. If a patient were put into an oxygen tent his distress might be lessened; he might become pink and peaceful; but quite frequently he entered a slumber which was irreversible.

LIGHT THROUGH THE FOG

Then in the early 1950s the smogs brought the problem into the limelight. Barach, Donald, and others had given us hints but, like many others, I was helped most by Keith Westlake and Tom Simpson who had large numbers of patients with respiratory failure to deal with at Chase Farm Hospital in Enfield. For many years Tom had taken a lonely interest in the problem and Keith became his house physician in time for the winter "crop" of 1950–1. Although not as infamous as the smog of 1952, from their point of view it was a good year. Whenever I visited Chase Farm there were two or three patients with respiratory failure in the wards and on occasion there might be as many as a dozen. Ironically, the busier the hospital became the less easy it was to be sure of the diagnosis because there was not time to measure the blood gases.

Westlake became engrossed in the problem and stayed on at Chase Farm with the support of a British Medical Association Ernest Hart memorial fellowship. With Simpson and Kaye, Westlake performed a heroic feat of clinical investigation. They had a large and busy general medical service which was further strained by a great many patients with respiratory failure. They had no technical help and their equipment – as good as any then available – was primitive by today's standards. Using a temperamental pH meter and a Van Slyke apparatus, they followed the changes in carbon dioxide tension and in cerebrospinal fluid pressure on giving oxygen. They recorded changes in the former which at least one physiologist proclaimed must be incorrect because the values were incompatible with life. Clinicians were less surprised; I suspect because they hadn't even heard of carbon dioxide tension.

The late 'forties and early 'fifties were great years in clinical research – when the application of physiology greatly improved understanding and management of renal failure, liver failure, electrolyte disturbances, and so on. The techniques were often simple or even crude by today's standards but these studies were an emotional strain. The patients were very ill; they came into hospital with little warning; and it was difficult to mobilise help in studying them. For all these reasons it was difficult to observe a protocol and furthermore one was often exploring in the dark without the guidance of a clear hypothesis. In our work on respiratory failure we would usually study patients in the late evening or at night and postpone those measurements that could wait. This approach might mean doing a dozen Van Slyke measurements of plasma carbon dioxide at the weekend.

VICTIMS OF ENTHUSIASM

By 1951 the dilemma of acute following on chronic (acute on chronic) respiratory failure was generally appreciated: the patients were at risk of death from anoxia but giving oxygen might cause cabon dioxide narcosis. The fate of the patients swung rapidly. From being victims of neglect, they became victims of enthusiasm. Oxygen was given by various devices according to various routines. One routine was to give it intermittently – with the idea that spells without it would stimulate the breathing and "blow off" the carbon dioxide. This routine was quite popular despite Haldane's sensible dictum that intermittent oxygen treatment is like bringing a drowning man to the surface...occasionally.

We tried other approaches haphazardly: intravenous bicarbonate, to raise the blood pH; artificial ventilation; stimulants; and tracheotomy. The old tank ventilators left over from the polio epidemics and the newer but primitive positive-pressure machines did not seem to be able to cope with the patients who "fought" them – probably because the machines did not provide enough ventilation. Furthermore, positive pressure ventilation was impossible to apply by mask to these restless, confused patients. Stimulants were nasty but seemed sometimes to reverse the drift into carbon dioxide narcosis. The dramatic step, of course, was tracheotomy.

Tracheotomy (making a hole in the windpipe) in these patients was (and often still is) a miserable business. The trachea (windpipe) jerked up and down, causing shearing forces between the tracheotomy tube, the trachea, and the soft tissues. A bruised, infected neck or, worst of all, erosion of the trachea was often the result. We now know that some damage to the trachea with stricture is common. Few patients survived tracheotomy but we suspected that the poor results were caused by delay in performing it. A surgical aphorism that acquired a certain currency was, "The right time to do a tracheotomy in these patients is when you first think of it." It was all very unsatisfactory and unpredictable but then we couldn't measure anything to see what we were doing.

I had returned from Johns Hopkins able to do Riley's bubble method of oxygen and carbon dioxide pressure measurements; I also had a grasp of the new understanding of the processes of gas exchange and their disturbances.

Late in 1955 Keith Westlake came to the Middlesex and we decided to try to tackle the problem of acute on chronic respiratory failure systematically, starting with stimulants. I wanted to try controlled oxygen treatment but the equipment for the bubble method would not be available for a few months and Keith was persuaded that the most important factor in the development of narcosis was central respiratory depression which he thought, on the strength of a few preliminary studies, might be reversed by nikethamide or aminophylline.

Our routine was to inspect the admission record each morning and evening to see if any potentially suitable patients had been admitted. This inspection would be followed by a tour of the wards to see if any patient admitted as having heart failure, pneumonia, or some other label was in fact suffering from undiagnosed respiratory failure. If we suspected that this was so we would seek out the patient's consultant and obtain permission to proceed. Some of the consultants were much more dubious about arterial puncture than about the administration of drugs. Indeed many of them regarded tracheotomy as perfectly laudable but arterial puncture as quite unjustifiable. We would also try to have the patient moved to our so called laboratory and persuade our ward sister to lend us a nurse for a couple of hours. Then, usually in the early evening, the study would begin.

Were this a Hollywood film script the action would be shrouded in dense yellow fog but in fact most of the patients came into hospital some days after the fog had lifted. Nevertheless there were occasional night studies when all parts of the hospital were murky; one could not see one end of the corridor from another and patients and staff were all coughing.

The protocol of our research was simple. A Riley arterial needle was inserted and two control samples of blood were taken. Their pH was measured and five ml were put in a screw top bottle in the refrigerator for Van Slyke analysis later that night, on the morrow, or whenever we could find time. Then the drug was given. In the case of aminophylline we gave a large but standard dose. In the case of nikethamide, however, we had nothing to guide us and had to resort to pushing the dose up until the patient's behaviour suggested that a stimulant concentration had been reached. Then there was often a hectic spell when the patient became agitated and restless. The twitches of the respiratory failure would rapidly change to much more extensive jerks which made it difficult to keep the needle in place and very difficult to draw an arterial sample. (Today's indwelling catheters make life much easier.) I would try to take samples every two or three minutes during the peak of the drug action and Keith would analyse them as quickly as he could. This frequency depended on the mood of the pH meter. If it was drifting or was difficult to balance, we might be able to get a credible reading only every five minutes or so. We had great difficulty in earthing both the machine and the operator, so that Keith had to stand barefooted in a tray of saline. Usually either Keith was chastising me for my failure to get blood samples or I was niggling him for his failure to analyse them quickly enough. Occasionally all went well and something like a protocol could be said to have been observed; more often the study had to be abandoned.

We managed only a handful of completed studies that winter, then Keith died. He was a severe manic depressive and for the last fortnight of his life he was intensely manic. Then one afternoon Nora, his wife, came home to find him stretched out on the bed smelling of almonds and quite dead. Had he become suddenly depressed or had he felt intimations of depression and decided to go while he still had the energy and the will? My own experience suggests the second possibility. There was certainly no evidence of planning and his way of going was very hard on Nora and his daughters, to whom he was devoted.

I wrote up the results and am grateful to the *British Medical Journal* for publishing the paper. Today the study would have no chance of being supported by a granting agency, cleared by an ethics committee, accepted by a statistician, or published by a journal. Even so, it was certainly persuasive in showing that the use of stimulants was not the answer to the problem, so I set off to explore controlled oxygen treatment. The difficulties of this study were, if anything, technically greater and they were more exhausting physically because they went on so long and the bubble method was very demanding. I do not, however, remember this work with the same distaste as the stimulant studies, which made both the patients and ourselves miserable and which at no stage gave us any sense of discovery. Nights spent with vacuum cleaners driven backwards into bags hanging over a patient's head (the prelude to the High Air flow with Oxygen Enrichment (HAFOE) principle and the Venturi mask) cannot really be taken as typical of the hospital experience of a patient in respiratory failure in the early 'fifties. It's another story.

Father's dying – when "low"

In 1952 Father told me he had carcinoma of the prostate and was taking oestrogens. He said his first symptom had been "reduplication of urination" (a second flow of urine after apparently ceasing) which his urologist had said was "typical". I have looked this up in a few texts and found no mention of it and I suspect he had made it up (he volunteered the story glibly as though rehearsed) and that he really had something more typical such as haemospermia (blood in the semen). But why should I think this? When would he have noticed haemospermia? Masturbation? After sex with Mrs P?

The years passed. Father became slightly eunuchoid but I don't remember much if any discussion of his cancer. We went on a holiday to Austria in September 1958 – Diana, he, and I. Memory of the trip is blurred but I seem to remember having some sort of difficulty in arranging the days and nights so as to please both of them. No memory of complaint or of trouble...just a vague feeling.

I have a vivid memory after we returned of shaking his hand in a country lane in Essex before he got into his car to drive off to Yorkshire. Then in late October or early November somebody, possibly Father himself, phoned to say he was in hospital in Bradford with urinary obstruction. I said I would go in a couple of days. I remember bursting into tears and quickly having to find a small room on the medical unit, to avoid embarrassment.

Train to Bradford. Ward sister an impressive Yorkshire-woman – not large but efficient and very concerned about Father's state of mind because she knew that he must sense that his cancer was out of control. In retrospect, I think she probably discussed this openly with him; she was opposed to his later nephrostomies.

At any rate she stage managed my arrival so as to ensure she and I had a talk before I was allowed to see Father. When she was satisfied, she took me to his room. He was lying apparently at ease but with two bottles under his bed which I gathered came from his ureters. One bottle was dripping fairly full and clear; the other was almost empty and the urine was cloudy. As I write, I remember the sister had prepared me for this. I am pretty sure I hadn't seen or spoken to the urologist... or perhaps I had. Anyway he had placed indwelling high ureteric catheters to get a urine flow while assessing Father's condition. The intention was to explore his abdomen in a few days.

Memory is blurred but I remember the urologist seeing me after this exploration and telling me that he was unable to do a ureteric-colic transplant or anything like that because the growth had surrounded both ureters up the posterior abdominal wall and the only thing he had been able to do was a bilateral nephrostomy.

"Does he know?" I asked.

"No. I'm leaving it for you to tell him" (or words to that effect). The point is that he made me break the news. Odd behaviour – or so it seemed.

I don't remember how I handled the situation. I seem to remember Father coming round, noticing he had tubes in the region of his penis and being distressed when I told him he now had nephrostomies.

A surgeon's prayer: "Oh God, take me not through my bladder."

For the next few weeks Brian and I took it in turns to spend the weekends at Father's bedside. His condition was pretty static. The right kidney worked; the left didn't. He weakened. Very demanding and miserable weekends. Awful trains. Trying to read. Trying to talk.

On one visit he told me that Mother would have to come back if he was to go home. I remember being distressed by this. He had found it difficult to tolerate her when he was fit. Could he stand her fussing over him? Anyway, it came about.

Brian and Diana took Mother to Harrogate and the next weekend, Diana and I took him from the hospital. Mother was very good and we left them being tender to each other. Diana was very pregnant: she had a brown maternity smock.

Further visits.

Wednesday 1 April, early evening. Mother phones. "He's gone. He went in my arms. He was quite peaceful."

Funeral 4 April – Brian's birthday – wept copiously, very embarrassed.

Controlling oxygen

In 1952 two thousand people died in the Great Smog of London. I was a lecturer in physiology and a part-time registrar and saw a number of these patients but could make no measurements. We tried to treat them with ventilators, which were of no value, and by tracheotomy, which we felt we usually did too late. What I learned about acute on chronic respiratory failure that winter, I learned from Westlake (see *Respiratory failure in the 'fifties*).

After Keith Westlake died I pursued the idea of using controlled oxygen with the idea of identifying those patients who needed early tracheotomy as soon as possible. The proper study was technically difficult because it required large quantities of accurately prepared gas mixtures. Then I stumbled upon the idea of High Air Flow with Oxygen Enrichment (HAFOE). The idea was to supply oxygen at a known flow rate and add to that oxygen a known flow of air so that the mixture could be prescribed. By supplying the mixture at a high enough flow rate, it was possible to ensure that the patient breathed nothing else. The equipment I used was primitive. An old Electrolux vacuum cleaner controlled by a rheostat had its exhaust passed through a length of one inch diameter tubing and a two-way tap, used for fine adjustment of the flow, to a plastic clothes bag dangled from a piece of plywood. I ran the mixture at one hundred and twenty litres per minute, making the equipment very noisy.

With this equipment I made the fundamental measurements that were published in the *Lancet* in 1961. The physiology of the idea was OK, but what about the technology?

In July 1959, on the road to Oxford near High Wycombe, John Nunn, my good friend in anaesthesia, asked me from the back of the car, "Have you thought of using the Venturi principle which, as you know, is an adaptation of the Bernouilli theorem?"

"Yes I have, but I don't think you can get the necessary entrainment ratio."

John thought, however, that we could get such an entrainment ratio and suggested that I call Pat Williams of Oxygenaire. Pat Williams turned out to be a rubicund Irishman of considerable entrepreneurial drive, and he, in turn, introduced me to Freddy Croasdaile. Freddy Croasdaile requires as much credit for the Venturi mask as I do. When I met him he was aged about sixty; a bachelor of stooping gait and flappy feet. He had grey hair streamlined over his balding pate and the face of a sad but thoughtful dachshund. His hands were always in motion, shaping imaginary equipment.

I asked him, "Is it possible to get a twenty to one or even a ten to one entrainment ratio?" He said it was and that afternoon he made me a single Venturi tube which he said had an entrainment ratio of ten to one. Using the simple Scholander apparatus I made one or two measurements which suggested that at a constant flow of four litres per minute it would indeed produce a concentration of 27.5% oxygen, implying an entrainment ratio of ten to one.

Next day he produced a gated Venturi made of brass which I still have and which gives concentrations of 24, 28, and 35% oxygen. We used this to supply the mixture through a three quarter inch diameter tube to the same primitive head tent. (We were now making quite a number of these from bags, bought in Oxford Street at one and sixpence a time.)

One day Freddy said to me, "Can I try and build the Venturi into a mask?" It had never occurred to me that it might be possible. He came back a week later with quite a light mask onto which he had cemented a Venturi tube. I tested this mask, as a result of which I produced a paper also published in the *Lancet*. This mask was found to have several defects and it turned out to be easier to make a range of disposable masks than a mask with variable concentrations.

Oxygenaire were taken over by Vickers Medical in 1963; the collaboration between myself and Vickers was good but never the same. Incidentally, I still have the briefcase which was the only remuneration I ever received from Oxygenaire for the design of the Venturi mask. The trade in Venturi masks, now made by several firms, is worth several million dollars a year!

In 1967, due to the enthusiasm of Dr Carl Muschenheim and Dr Alvin Barach, two typical but very different New York physicians, I was invited to give the Burns Amberson Lecture to the American Thoracic Society on the treatment of acute on chronic respiratory failure. This was a signal honour in that I was the first non-American and much the youngest person ever to be invited to give this lecture.

Both Carl Muschenheim and Al Barach have since died. Al Barach, in particular, was a marvellous rogue. The literature from 1920 to 1975 is littered with his papers: in these it is as difficult to follow his ideas as it is to follow a flea in a French hotel bed!

Today there are several so called Venturi masks on the market but they have never been tested with the rigour Freddy and I gave to the original Venturi masks between 1959 and 1967, and I'm afraid to say that some of them really do not work. I'm not prepared, however, to spend my remaining years "doing a Ralph Nader" on oxygen equipment.

Daddy says do a P_{CO_2}

Measurement of the pressure of carbon dioxide in the blood – the P_{CO_2} – is important for two main reasons. Firstly it reflects the adequacy of the volume of breathing in relation to the needs of the body. Secondly carbon dioxide combines with water to form carbonic acid and thus changes in P_{CO_2} affect the acidity of the blood. In guiding the use of oxygen in patients with acute on chronic respiratory failure the measurement of the P_{CO_2} can be vital and the strategy I had evolved for the use of controlled oxygen treatment depended on its use. At that time, however, in the mid-1950s, measurement of P_{CO_2} was very difficult and was used only in research. Thanks to Dick Riley, I was almost alone in applying the P_{CO_2} in acute medical practice. So my decision to go public with the use of controlled oxygen therapy was frustrated. Then in 1956 an American, Clarence Collier, described a "rebreathing" method for measuring P_{CO_2}. Rebreathing means just that – breathing in and out of a small container such as a bag. Using a rapid carbon dioxide analyser, Collier showed what had been suspected for many years, that if one rebreathed from a bag, starting with an appropriate P_{CO_2}, an equilibrium was obtained with the blood entering the lung (the mixed venous blood). This equilibrium was recognised by a "plateau" in the record of P_{CO_2} measured at the mouth: as the breath went in and out between the lungs and the bag there was no change in the P_{CO_2}. He also recognised that the difference in P_{CO_2} between this mixed venous blood and the arterial blood (which for various reasons is preferable to the mixed venous P_{CO_2}) was small and relatively constant in resting subjects.

Clearly Collier's method would be a godsend, not only in

guiding controlled oxygen treatment but also in diagnosing and managing respiratory failure of all causes. We could not afford a rapid carbon dioxide analyser, however, so Jack and I approached Mr Bartlett of the Infra-red Development Company to persuade him that if we could borrow an analyser and repeat Collier's work we might open up a whole new market for him. He was somewhat sceptical but agreed to let us have a rapid analyser for a few weeks.

We were able to repeat Collier's observation on ourselves, using a standard mixture of 7% carbon dioxide in oxygen which was generally available in the hospital. But how were we going to test the method in people whose P_{CO_2} was either too high or too low to reach equilibration with 7% carbon dioxide? It wasn't too difficult to prepare mixtures with a lower P_{CO_2} simply by diluting the 7% mixture. The preparation of more concentrated mixtures presented a problem. We found, however, that by rebreathing for a long time, the P_{CO_2} could be built up in a predictable way that was dependent chiefly on the duration of the rebreathing rather than on the initial P_{CO_2}. We thus evolved a "two stage" method in which the subject rebreathed oxygen for a minute and a half and then, after two or three minutes to "blow off" carbon dioxide, rebreathed the gas mixture he himself had so prepared for another twenty seconds. This procedure almost always produced a plateau. We checked the method in a number of patients with widely differing P_{CO_2}s. Jack did the rebreathing and I performed the bubble measurement. These studies were usually done in the evening and sometimes went on very late. On one occasion we were studying a nice old lady with respiratory failure who thought that Jack was her own personal Dr Kildare and kept interrupting the procedure to tell him so. Jack was able to get measurements but not according to the protocol we had agreed. Close to midnight, as I was finishing the last bubble measurement, he staggered into the lab pushing the carbon dioxide analyser. "I've thought of a title for the paper: 'A rapid, easy, bedside method for measuring P_{CO_2}'."

Now, of course, these observations had shown the rapid

analyser was not essential as provided one went through the two stage procedure, any simple chemical analyser would do.

Naturally Mr Bartlett was not entirely pleased by this turn of events and as he wanted his rapid analyser for further development we reluctantly returned it. We were against returning it for three reasons. Although the two stage method worked, it was not as convenient or as convincing as Collier's method. Secondly we had made some very intriguing observations about the way P_{CO_2} changes during rebreathing which we wanted to follow up and which, in fact, together with various co-workers, I did follow up in the next ten years or so. Thirdly, although there were several simple chemical analysers on the market, none seemed to combine the requisite accuracy with the ruggedness which would be needed for a piece of equipment handled by junior house staff. I therefore modified the classical Haldane apparatus and persuaded Aimer Products of Camden Town to manufacture it. So from being an unattainable research measurement, the P_{CO_2} became something which could be measured in five to ten minutes by a houseman with equipment costing fifteen pounds. We described all this in the *British Medical Journal* and the method enjoyed a brief popularity but was superceded by blood gas electrodes which require less skill. The rebreathing method, whether ours, Collier's, or any other, had, however, a number of advantages both theoretical and practical and is still used in many parts of the world.

In its heyday, our housemen had a rebreathing bag in their white coat pockets, in addition to the stethoscope. It is said that when the phone rang in our little flat Fiona, aged 4, would grab it and say: "Daddy says do a P_{CO_2}".

"A being breathing thoughtful breaths"*

Stuck up on the wall above my desk in the medical unit of the Middlesex were three photographs torn out of various newspapers; they were of three main sex symbols of the time Brigitte Bardot, Diana Dors, and Marilyn Monroe. To the third was stapled another newspaper clipping which said, "I never wear a brassiere because I believe in giving free play to my respiratory center."

As a respiratory physiologist I was always breathing out of tubes, through valves, and taps, and other things and I became very good at detecting slight obstructions due to kinks or other blockages. It seemed to me that it was unlikely that the Maker had equipped me with the sensory system to do this any more than it had equipped Marilyn with the ability to detect additions to the thoracic loads she normally had to move with each breath.

I discussed this idea with Stan, Paul, and Michael, three students who had taken a year off to do a degree in physiology and whom I had come to know pretty well. We decided to set out to measure our ability to detect what we subsequently came to call "additional external loads" to normal breathing. We decided to begin with the simple question: "How much stiffer does your chest have to be before you can feel it?" In some ways the chest and lungs resemble an elastic balloon or bellows; we wanted to mimic a less elastic or stiffer balloon. Following the hint given by Marilyn Monroe was no good because when you strap things around the chest you get all sorts of clues from pressures on the skin, joints, etc. It is not feasible to make the lungs themselves stiffer experimentally

*William Wordsworth, *She was a Phantom of Delight*.

so we turned to the empty, rigid container. If air is removed from a rigid container the pressure within it falls. The greater the amount of air removed the greater the fall in pressure; furthermore, the smaller the container the greater the fall in pressure for any given volume. We decided to breathe out of empty oil drums and find out how small the oil drums had to be before we "knew they were there". At the start the experiment seemed to be very easy, all one had to do was have a mouthpiece and a tap which was connected either to the outside air or to an oil drum. With the subject blindfolded, one of us would every now and then turn the tap from the air to the oil drum and see if he could feel the difference. We began by scrounging a couple of empty, twenty five gallon drums, which had been filled with some detergent, from the hospital dispensary, some lengths of discarded tubing from an anaesthetic machine, and one or two breathing taps from the physiology department. Nicky, the head of the students' laboratory in the physiology department, was always prepared to lend a bit of equipment as long as he had it back when the students were doing their breathing experiments.

Nicky was also very ingenious at making equipment from all manner of household articles. To do the experiment properly we needed to be able to measure the pressure in the oil drum. From this, using Boyle's law, we would be able to work out the depth of breathing and the effects of the oil drum on the depth of breathing. The measurement of a steady pressure is, of course, easy. You simply have water or mercury in a "U tube" similar to those used to measure barometric or blood pressure. These don't, however, respond quickly enough to changes in pressure for our requirements. At that time electric manometers had become fairly generally available and I had used them at Hopkins. Although we could have scrounged one, we decided to approach the problem in a simpler way. We took the lid of a jam jar and Nicky welded a piece of brass tubing into it. We stretched a piece of rubber from an old surgical glove over the lid, secured it with some elastic bands, and put a piece of cork on the middle. Then we took a drinking straw as a lever to rest on the cork and with a few bits and pieces from the physiology lab we managed to obtain an ink record on a piece of paper which was turned slowly on a drum called a Kymograph.

We put all this together one evening and tried it out. It proved easy to detect twenty five gallons. There then followed a long search for drums and taps as we found how embarrassingly easy it was to detect even quite large drums. We moved from the twenty five gallon to the forty and fifty gallon drums as our basic construction units and eventually we had an assembly of drums which totalled a hundred and sixty five imperial gallons. To enable us to "narrow down", we also had some five gallon drums as "fine adjustment". For those who now think metric or who, despite driving on the continent, have difficulty converting from gallons to litres, this all adds up to seven hundred and fifty litres. Those in the breathing business will appreciate that the "compliance" of the system was seven hundred and fifty ml per centimeter of water. Compliance is a measure of "give". We found it more convenient to look at things the other way round, as "stiffness", and express this again for those in the breathing business as "elastance". At this point, I might as well quote from the scientific paper we published a year or two later:

The values of the elastances to be used in the experiments were determined from the results of preliminary trials. An elastance of 4.9 cm H_2O/l (equivalent to a volume of 204 l) was chosen as the highest to be used because it was found to be the smallest value at which 100 per cent detection regularly occurred. Similarly, 1.4 cm H_2O/l (726 l) was chosen as the lower limit because it was the highest value at which no significant detection took place. The selected intermediate values were 4.0, 3.45, 2.6 and 2.0 cm H_2O/l (equivalent to volumes of 250, 295, 386 and 500 l respectively). They represent as even a gradation as could be achieved using units of 5 Imp Gal.

That sounds quite straightforward and it wasn't really difficult to get the drums by scrounging from various store rooms in the hospital and borrowing some of the bigger ones from a neighbouring building site. The taps, however, presented a problem. If you are going to breathe through them comfortably, taps must be wide bore, smooth in their operation, and as light as possible. As taps like these cost £7 each at the time we reached the bounds of Nicky's generosity. By turning to the hospital plumbers for help, however, we got a few big ones which we could mount in places where their weight didn't matter, and for the rest we turned to Proops. Proops is, or was, a shop in the Tottenham Court Road that sold war surplus equipment. In the back part of the store were marvellous boxes full of old aeroplane equipment including valves and taps to regulate the flow of petrol, or whatever the planes flew on in those days, to the engines. These I bought at twenty five shillings each with a temporary loan from the Campbell fund.

When this was all assembled, the experimenter was sitting in the middle of a set of drums with various taps within easy reach so that he could manipulate the different volumes. The floor area of the laboratory was almost entirely occupied by drums; initially to the amusement, and later to the irritation of others sharing the lab. When an experiment was in progress, the operator looked like a one man, West Indian steel band or the tympanist in some bizarre orchestra. Aesthetically the whole effect was rather pleasing because the drums varied in colour from a rich Etruscan through various oranges, yellows, and greens to a nice deep royal blue.

During the experiment, however, the contrast with a steel band was absolute. Silence was essential. The slightest rustle of the experimenter's clothing as he turned the taps could give the subject clues that something was about to happen. Eventually we solved the instrumental and technical problems and in the evening experiments, after the students had finished their lectures and I had finished seeing the patients, we knocked off a series of studies which took only about eight hours in all.

We found to our surprise that we could get reproducible results not only in an individual subject but also between subjects ("the intra and intersubject reproducibility was of a satisfactorily high order"). They all detected three hundred and eight odd litres (about eighty gallons) on about half the times we "turned them in".

As I have said, we began these experiments without any clear idea in mind. I think we had expected simply to find the pressure the subject had to develop before he could "feel" the drums. When we came to look at the results, however, we found the pressures the subjects were developing were really rather small, and certainly small in relation to the variation in pressures they were developing spontaneously. In other words the variation in their ordinary breathing must have meant that their chest muscles were developing pressures that varied more than the extra oil drums caused. I suppose we had also thought that the oil drums might reduce the size of breath the subject took and that is what he felt. The reduction in the size of breath caused by the drum was negligible, however. Eventually the penny dropped. It sounds so simple now but we eventually concluded that they could feel the drum because there was a change in the relation of volume to pressure. Some little man somewhere in the brain was saying: "for the volume of breath I have taken in, the pressure that I have to develop is bigger than I had expected." Now volume is three dimensional and pressure is two dimensional. To reduce the idea to simpler proportions, we expressed the idea as "length: tension appropriateness". Essentially we suggested that the relation between the force or tension that a subject's breathing muscles had to make to the change in length of some sensing system somewhere was not what he usually expected. If the degree of "inappropriateness" reached a certain level, then the normally unconscious effort of breathing became conscious.

We presented these results to some learned societies. In Britain they met with mild interest but of course the real test was how they would go down in the States, which was where all the leading respiratory physiologists (including the British ones) worked. I obtained a small travel grant to visit the States to discuss this research and other more serious work I was doing and took the opportunity to present the experiments to the annual meeting of the American Physiological Society. This is a huge meeting and one which I had not attended before. It meant speaking to about five hundred people in a ballroom in a downtown Chicago hotel. With trepidation I decided to show our equipment on a coloured slide. This was not at all according to form because in scientific meetings work was generally presented in black and white diagrams with the minimum of atmosphere. The beginning of my paper went quite well, however, in that at least people were amused. Having talked for the allotted ten minutes one expects either critical questions or downright hostility; I was met with a resounding silence. For a few hours I felt crushed but as people drifted up to me in the various bars at the hotel to ask questions they had not dared to ask in public I became increasingly confident that we really were on to something. When I got home, therefore, together with another group of students, who subsequently won an American prize for an essay they wrote on the work, I did some more experiments using tubes as well as drums. This time Jack Howell also joined in and we used the oil drums not only to study sensation but also their effects on the breathing of unconscious subjects. For this we needed a portable set which we put together from space frame and mounted on a disused food trolly we found in the hospital basement. We aroused a certain amount of interest as we pushed this bizarre piece of equipment back and forth across the hospital on our way to and from the operating rooms.

The motivation for all this work was to try to improve our understanding of the control of breathing. How does the breathing stay stable in the face of all the various loads caused by changing one's position, carrying things, lying down, or even wearing tight brassieres?

A couple of years later, I was asked to take part in a Ciba symposium to celebrate the hundred and first anniversary of the birth of JS Haldane. JS Haldane was one of the greatest pioneers in respiratory physiology. In addition to providing many of our basic ideas he also did very important practical work on the hazards of coal mines and on poison gases during the First World War. The symposium was very select: only about forty people were invited. I suspect I only made it because I happened to live and work half a mile from where it was being held and my expenses would be modest. Although we reported our studies as a contribution to the understanding of the control of breathing, I hinted in my concluding remarks that they might have some bearing on the sensation of breathlessness or dyspnoea (difficulty in breathing) felt by patients with lung or heart disease. This sensation is a particularly intriguing problem because not only does it affect normal people, it is also something which as doctors we are called upon to try to relieve. In the discussion much more attention was devoted to the implications of our work for the understanding of breathlessness than to the bearing it had on our understanding of the control of breathing. In subsequent reports of this symposium Jack and I both felt that we were over-interpreted and misinterpreted and eventually we wrote the following letter to the editor of the *British Medical Journal*:

A respiratory physiologist offering a unitary explanation for breathlessness should arouse the same suspicions as a tattooed archbishop offering a free ticket to Heaven. But the euphoria is such that we are only a little sad that neither the writer of your annotation (August 10, p 336) nor 'other experts' have fully grasped the system of our delusion. They are right to seize on the word 'inappropriate' which is certainly the key, but why try it on only the outer doors of the mystery?

At the risk of increasing confusion, the hypothesis can be explained as follows: dyspnoea may be experienced (1) if the neurochemical demand for breathing is inappropriate to the apparent needs (as at altitude), (2) if the neuromuscular effort of breathing is inappropriate to the breathing that is achieved (as in asthma), or (3) if the neural effort is inappropriate to the muscular act that is achieved (as in muscular paralysis). On close examination, the messages in all these three states are not dissimilar. Moreover, in most clinical conditions there would be a mixture of two or three, so the sensation reaching consciousness may be compound or impure.

We do not suggest that "some centre of consciousness is continuously relating the demand for ventilation to the actual ventilation". We, in fact, suggest that the relations listed above are being continuously sensed unconsciously because the adjustment of breathing requires that they must be. Should there be more than a certain degree of inappropriateness, it reaches consciousness and should it be excessive, it causes distress.

We are not yet sure if this is a good hypothesis because we do not yet see how to test it conclusively. But, should the explanation be of this nature, dyspnoea would not be fundamentally different from annoyances such as aspirating with a stiff syringe, cutting with a blunt knife, driving with fading brakes, or serving with a slack racquet, except that one must breathe.

A year or so after the Haldane symposium I was asked to help edit an issue of the *British Medical Bulletin*, a prestigious publication of the British Council. Three issues are published each year and each is devoted to a field of medicine in which there have been important advances and to which the British contribution has been notable. It is not only a national "show case" but a respected and valuable one. Because of the interest aroused at and after the Haldane symposium Jack and I were asked to contribute a review of our understanding of breathlessness. We agreed and attempted to push the idea of "length: tension inappropriateness" to the limit. I outlined the first draft and sent it to Jack who was now in Manchester. During the gestation of the article he came to London occasionally, each time with criticisms of what I had sent him, and we argued for hours. Once, when the deadline for completion was getting uncomfortably close, we went on for most of the night. After each visit I would attempt to pull things together and send him another draft but we also ran up quite sizeable phone bills despite the careful observation of the cheap call rate at night and on Sundays. Eventually we thrashed something out which I still think is about as good as we could have done at that time.

In Manchester, Jack had rapidly developed a large practice of all sorts of patients with chest disease and was investigating various new compounds that were being introduced for the relief of asthma. One of the firms for whom he had done a good job (that is, he had shown in a careful study that their new drug was better than those currently available) offered to sponsor a symposium. I think they hoped it would be an occasion to promote their product. Jack, however, persuaded them that their reputation would be more enhanced, albeit indirectly, by supporting a three day, international symposium to discuss "breathlessness". Those unfamiliar with medicine may wonder how such a subject could attract people for three days; in fact the problem was to select from among those wishing to come. Jack was determined that the number of participants would be small, a dozen big speakers and no more than thirty other discussants. He also ensured that the physical arrangements and timing would enable participants to discuss the subject rather than, as can often happen, simply allow the speakers to give their papers followed by a brief discussion. In these aims we were following the style of the famous Ciba Foundation which had developed the symposium to a fine art. Thanks to Jack's flair, which in addition included a certain amount of "question planting" among the participants and "fixing" of the chairmen to quieten the loquacious and draw out the taciturn, the meeting was a resounding success. Thanks to the further generosity of the sponsors the proceedings were published. Then again Jack's flair showed itself. We cut and arranged the transcripts of the tape recordings to achieve a "truthful" if not literally true record without losing the cut and thrust and flavour of the discussions. We sent our edited version to all the participants together with the "raw" transcripts of what they actually had said. With a few exceptions, which were easily dealt with, all the speakers thanked us for having written what they intended to say.

I think we can claim that, like the symposium, the book itself was a success. It pulled the subject together, was the standard account of "the state of the art" in 1965, and has prompted much subsequent research.

We had a little difficulty with participants whose native tongue was not English both at the meeting and in the transcript. At that time it was customary at international meetings to have simultaneous translation in French and German; we could not afford this luxury, however, and by and large all the leading figures spoke Engligh pretty well. There was one large, red headed Belgian whose name was Little (in French) and who, although he understood English very well, was diffident about addressing us in English. We arranged, therefore, for a Frenchman to read the paper to us in English while Professor Little stood behind him and pointed out the relevant information on the slides of his experiments projected on the screen. Unfortunately the reader kept losing his way in the heavily annotated manuscript. When he heard a mistake, Professor Little rapped his translator on the shoulder with the long wooden pointer. As the mistakes increased, synchronisation between text and pictures was sometimes lost. The raps became increasingly frequent, changing first to prods and then firm thrusts in the speaker's back, provoking muttered exchanges in French and, of course, frequent Gallic shrugs of the translator's shoulders as he struggled with the text.

When we came to edit the transcript we had trouble with the translator's own paper. He is the Charles Boyer of respiratory physiology and speaks perfect English but with the accent of Maurice Chevalier. His work had required him to study the effects of oxygen on the breathing of people living at high altitudes in the Peruvian Andes. He had used a test in which the subject took two breaths of oxygen in the rarefied air. He called this the "two breath test" and had applied it to most of the inhabitants of a village in the Altoplano. In his talk, distorted by the microphones, tape recorders, and the hearing of the typist, this became the "two breast test". ("We went round zee village giving all zee natives – particularly zee young ones – zee two breast test.") The typist had coped with the zee's but not with the breasts. Jack was editing in Manchester and I in London. Late one night the phone range and such was our empathy that when I heard Jack's voice and the suppressed mirth as he asked, "Have you come to...?", I immediately knew what he meant.

After the Manchester symposium, Jack and I became "experts": whenever anybody wanted a talk on breathlessness one of us was invited. The fact that we were invited meant, of course, that we became even more confirmed as experts (at any rate in other people's view). I suppose you could call this "becoming an expert by positive feedback". I have lectured on the subject from Aberdeen to Auckland and from Berlin to Buenos Aires.

Being an expert also has its scientific benefits. People often told us about their observations on patients and their experiments or asked questions which probed our understanding. This occasionally led to other experiments like, "How long can you hold your breath when you are completely paralysed and cannot take a breath even when you want to?" But that's another story.

I have had a lot of fun and got a lot of mileage out of those few hours spent with a few students and a few discarded oil drums.

Doctors' wives are difficult patients

I have left this piece much as it was written – three weeks after we had had a road accident, while Diana was in hospital and I was pretty manic.

9 pm, 22 August 1982.
Pete Fountain, "Old Man River": "You gets a little drunk and you lands in jail." Diana gave me this disc when we went to New Orleans to lecture to the refresher course on chest diseases ten years ago, after we got the last table at Pete's Place.

Must exhaust myself tonight because tomorrow I am having a sleep study to see if a disturbance of my sleep may be playing an important part in my manic moods. Must give the tests the best chance of being decisive.

Pipe drawing too well – feeling a little nauseated.

Set myself the goal of typing all night – or until I pass out.

"Basin Street Blues": "The place where the dark and the light folk meet." Earlier today decided to tell the story of Mrs D. Rest awhile and try to find the right opening.

"Way down yonder in New Orleans", great rhythm section. "Those ladies with flashing eyes: stop a little while" – I might if my wife wasn't with me.

"Tin Roof Blues" – one of the best phrases in jazz.

Decide to start the serious business of the night with Ella and Louis; but first a change of mood: "Che gelina manina" – Pavarotti. Memories of Covent Garden and the Dickinsons – and of course, Diana – always Diana. She phoned tonight, tearful but better; no fever and the spasms of pain from her broken back are easier. Let's have some Verdi: "Aida" loud as the speakers will take it. Was Verdi present at the first performance in Cairo? If so, how did he feel? If I were depressed, I would envy him – but not now.

And for good measure, "La donna e mobile" – memories of Quilico and Warlock.

Cool it with Ella, Basie, and "Honeysuckle Rose", then "Do I want you? 'Deed I do".

"Into each life some rain must fall." Ella and Basie, the greatest riffing I have.

How will I maintain the right mood and the right flow? Try one third brandy and two thirds soda.

"You've got a certain way of flirting with them there eyes. They're gonna get you in a whole lot of trouble – them there eyes."

"Tea for Two"; how marvellous that a song written for a light musical can provide the raw material for such good jazz!

And now down to serious business: Ella and Louis: "Cheek to Cheek"; Astaire and Rogers circa 1936 and my first dance lessons.

10.15 pm. "They all laughed at me wanting you."

I did not know Mrs D either professionally or socially but like many people at the Hammersmith, I knew about her. She was the wife of one of the university lecturers in pathology. She was a physiotherapist by profession, the mother of two young children, and she was slowly dying of what was said to be a progressive and untreatable degenerative condition of the nerves controlling her vital functions – swallowing and breathing. She could no longer even hold her head up.

"Autumn in New York."

One misty autumn Friday afternoon in 1966 or 1967, Charles Fletcher came into my office and told me Mrs D was coming into the hospital that afternoon in a pretty bad way and as he was off on holiday, would I look after her. "But don't strive too officiously...."

"He's going to turn me down and say 'can't we be friends?'"

She was brought into the ward about 2.30 pm in the middle of my teaching round in a terrible state: barely conscious, in great distress, so blue as to be almost black, and with the death rattle in her breathing. I immediately dismissed the students and quickly went over her. Terminal she may have been but this was no way to go. I called for a laryngoscope and an endotracheal tube and tried to give her an airway but I could not get her to extend her neck – it caused spasm and terrible pain she whispered to me.

"Love divided in two don't do." "Let's call the whole thing off."

I asked our registrar, Satinder (Seth) Lal, to have a go because I knew he was technically slicker than I. He had to use a degree of force that made Mrs D moan and made me wince but he succeeded and after a few squeezes of the oxygen bag her colour "pinked up" and her face assumed a semblance of peace.

"It's not the pale moon that excites me... it's the nearness of you."

We did a rebreathing P_{CO_2} measurement. It was 90 – over twice the normal value – and verging on the dangerous so we gave her some artificial ventilation (without much difficulty – surprise). We lowered her P_{CO_2} to about 60 and then stopped using the ventilator. She made no effort to breathe. We made sure she had enough oxygen and waited ten minutes but she still did not breathe and her P_{CO_2} was greater than the range of the analyzer – over 110. She lost consciousness but this didn't worry me because she had plenty of oxygen "on board" and her colour was a healthy pink.

"You've had your first lesson in learning the blues."
11 pm. Getting tired. Mild night. Stopped raining. Take dog out and get some fresh air.

162

11.15 pm. Back to it. Take a few minutes to get pipe going well and to replenish the B and S (only one glass so far).

"The way you sip your tea...they can't take that away from me."

We restarted artificial ventilation and once her Pco_2 reached 50 Mrs D regained consciousness and indicated that she wanted her neck supported. We put two pillows under her neck – and surprise – she began to breathe feebly but on her own.

"I won't dance don't ask me."

Despite the encouraging evidence of her spontaneous breathing, we could not trust to nature and put her back on a ventilator. In an hour or so we had her condition stabilised with a Pco_2 between 40 and 50 and she indicated that she was in no pain. Then I went through her past record with a fine tooth comb because the diagnosis of motor neurone disease just didn't make sense to me.

"A Foggy Day in London Town" – and it was.

I found the evidence I had been looking for. She had had x-rays taken after she had swallowed some radio-opaque barium to investigate her difficulty in swallowing. The barium had filled the bronchial tubes and there was no record of her having coughed, spluttered, or in any way manifested that it was going down the wrong tube. The implication was that she had lost sensation in her throat. I went back, there-fore, and examined her throat and sure enough I could press as hard as I liked with a tongue depressor and she didn't gag.

"A Fine Romance." If I am ever Roy Plommetted onto that desert island, this and "Beethoven's Sixth" will be top of my list.

12.15 am. Start the "Pastorale".

Conclusion: this is not a motor neurone disease as there is

too much evidence of loss of sensory functions. But the diagnosis had been made by Lord Brain, the most distinguished neurologist in the country and it was now late on a Friday afternoon. I examined her again more thoroughly than I had been able to in the earlier panic and decided we could see her through the weekend – indeed we could get her chest in better shape with some intensive physiotherapy. I had a guardedly optimistic talk with her husband and hinted at my doubts. He agreed that I could call on Lord Brain and anyone else I like. I first tried to get Chris Pallis, our own neurologist, but he was unavailable so I called Mr Valentine Logue whom I had known at the Middlesex. He was not particularly encouraging but after all why should he take the opinion of a junior chest doctor over that of the greatest neurologist in the land? I got him to agree, however, to see Mrs D on the Monday, provided Lord Brain also agreed. With considerable apprehension, therefore, and not a little difficulty, I tracked His Lordship down as he was about to leave home for some grand official dinner. I introduced myself by saying we had met twice before when, in his capacity as President of the Royal College of Physicians, he had firstly failed me and then secondly passed me in the MRCP examination. I need not have worried. He said that of course he remembered Mrs D and was not happy about the diagnosis. He would cancel his appointments for Monday afternoon and meet me and Mr Logue at the Hammersmith at 5 pm. "After all, she is a doctor's wife and we all know that if anything can go wrong it will go wrong with relatives of the profession."

1 am. Take five minutes to light another pipe, refill the glass, and wallow in Beethoven's "Sturm and Frohe und dankbare Gefuhle nach derr, Sturm". What next? Flick through the cabinet (Diana made it at evening class last winter) and come across Cleo Laine – "Shakespeare and All that Jazz".
"Be bloody, bold and resolute."
1.15–2.15 am. Relax, sip double Balbec (too young), and smoke while listening first to Cleo and then to Wolfgang Amadeus's piano concertos 17 and 21. Memories of the

Academy Oxford Street and of course of Diana. "Elvira Madigan" – he shot her correctly.

The memories of the Monday and the Tuesday are forming with marvellous clarity. I hope I can capture them.

2 am. Rusty, the beloved family hound, who looks like a cross between an Alsatian and a Dachshund, whines his insistence for another turn round the block, a lovely mild night. Also put out the garbage for collection in the morning.

2.30 am. Very cool. Memories and words well forming. No need for alcohol. Let there be iced water. And God saw that it was good.

2.45 am. John Handy, "Dancy Dancy", memories of flying into San Francisco from Cincinnati after my "success" at the American Thoracic Society in 1967.

2.50 am. Back to the third of my DE discs – "Duke Ellington's Greatest Hits" (what a lousy title for a great record, but there's no denying the truth of it). The high spot is the "A Train" sung by Betty Roche, one of my favourite bits of jazz singing. And then the Duke picking the notes of "Solitude".

Don't be under any misconception; the story of Mrs D is forming all the time.

3.00 am. Sudden craving for Mahler's "Fourth". Sorry Duke. Am now ready for the home stretch.

Stuck closely by Mrs D throughout the weekend. Found that in addition to her other problems she was losing sodium (salt) in large amounts in her urine. I gave her a generous intravenous drip with gratifying improvement in her general condition; she was even able to breathe on her own for an hour or so.

Mr L arrived at 4 pm on Monday afternoon. I suspect he wanted to go over Mrs D before facing Lord B. He was a strikingly handsome man with grey eyes whose pupils were of unequal size and he had the valuable knack of looking at you as though you were the most important person he had ever met. It was said of him that he was really a neurologist to whom cutting was a regrettable necessity. His examination of Mrs D was an aesthetic treat and I was relieved to find that, while he dotted a few i's and crossed a few t's, in all essentials he confirmed my findings.

Lord B arrived shortly after 5 pm and checked a few of the sensory signs by which I laid great store. Then we retired to the dingy physicians' room and His Lordship put on his overcoat to keep out the ever present, damp cold of the Hammersmith.

Mr L was ever so respectful and stressed how closely the case must have resembled motor neurone disease when Lord B had first seen her. "But now there is clear evidence of deep seated mischief in the medulla – although God only knows what." Neurological exotica passed back and forth between them until I could contain myself no longer.

"With respect, and as a mere chest physician, it seems to be agreed that she has something local in the medulla (the very lowest and most vital part of the brain). The only hope is that it is surgically treatable so I think you, Mr Logue, should have her transferred to your unit at the Maida Vale Hospital. I am prepared to keep her alive from the breathing standpoint if you want to do more investigations but for God's sake don't take too long over them."

Mr L said that that was all very well but extensive investigations in the past, including numerous x-rays, had not shown anything and he did not relish the idea of blindly exploring the deepest and most vital part of the brain. We went round the circuit a couple more times with Mr L weakening and I getting more forceful and at about 7.30 pm he agreed that she should be transferred on the morrow and he would "go in and look" on the Wednesday morning.

We called in her poor husband who had been waiting all this time and Lord B gave him the news, including some complimentary remarks about me which did not come amiss in the next week.

3.30 am. Tired but not sleepy. Keep going while the memory flows. Mild oesophageal pain. Sip milk and absorb Schwarzkopf and "Sehr behaglich". "Wir geniessen die himmlischen Freuden..."

4 am. Brief altercation with Fiona who thinks I should go

*to bed or at least use the earphones so as not to disturb
everyone else. Agree and start Anita O'Day – more memories
of The Academy with Anita belting it out under a great straw
hat in "Jazz on a Summer's Afternoon". Pipe needs extensive decoking.*

*"The Party's Over." "Take off your makeup. Now you
must wake up."*

*Rusty demands a third walk. I accede because it clears my
head.*

I was relieved to learn that the anaesthetist at Maida Vale
was to be Jan Hewer whom I had known for years at the
Middlesex. I phoned him and gave him all the details (but in
retrospect, I should have paid more attention to the sodium
problem).

I sent Seth over in the ambulance with strict instructions to
make it clear that I was in no mood to observe the niceties of
hospital etiquette. I may not be on the staff of Maida Vale but
they were to bloody well call me if they had any respiratory
problems.

Wednesday noon Jan phoned me in great excitement. They
had found an Arnold-Chiari malformation and as soon as
Mr L relieved the pressure on the medulla, Mrs D began to
breathe virtually normally...and he had a record to prove it.

I was rather unclear on Arnold-Chiari malformations, but
gathered that the medulla is pulled down into the foramen
magnum, the big hole in the bottom of the skull through
which the spinal cord takes over from the brain. Mrs D's
medulla was pulled down two or three inches and was being
starved of blood while all the nerves coming out of the
medulla were either stretched, compressed, or both. As soon
as bone was chipped away to make the great hole somewhat
greater, everything started to improve.

I lived in St John's Wood so I went to the Maida Vale that
evening. I went to the head porter and asked where Mrs D
was. I was wearing a cloth cap, a very oilstained duffle coat,
and bicycle clips, so the porter told me rather offhandedly
that I would have to come back at the proper visiting hours.
I climbed onto my high horse and said I had been sent for by

Lord B. The porter was still suspicious and called someone on the internal phone. "Bloke here says he's come from the Hammersmith Hospital to see one of your patients." Pause. "No, he doesn't look like one; he's come on a bike." Pause. "All right, I'll send him up."

The story should end there but it didn't. Two days later I was phoned by a distraught Dr D, "She's going downhill and her breathing is irregular and I can't get them to do anything about it." I bicycled over and sure enough her breathing was not good. Fortunately, due to the influence of Jan, they had the wherewithal to do my method for PCO_2; it was 60. But why? The neurological lesion had been corrected. Then I remembered the trouble with the sodium. As was usual on neurological units, they were not paying enough attention to her sodium needs and in fact had her on a restricted salt intake as is standard in patients who have raised pressure in the brain. I summoned the anaesthetic registrar and made him give her assisted ventilation while I got the surgical houseman to put up an intravenous drip through which I poured in sodium at a rate that he was convinced would give her heart failure. In an hour, however, she was as right as rain and never looked back. When I last heard of her five years later, she was leading an entirely normal life.

I must admit to have been weeping gently through these last few paragraphs. Overly sentimental? Probably, but in a way the case of Mrs D is the apotheosis of my career. I combined clinical acumen with sound physiology, my own invention, and a fair amount of bloodymindedness to save the doctor's wife.

5.10 am. How to unwind? Café au diable with two fingers of scotch and Schwarzkopf singing "Heilige Nacht". And Rusty gets a fourth walk.

"Breath's a ware that will not keep"*

Breathlessness is a sensation known to everyone and it is also one of the commonest symptoms of disease. It is not surprising, therefore, that as our understanding of respiration has increased, those in the breathing business like to wonder if they understand the causes of this sensation any better.

I seems to me that, in very general terms, an understanding of breathlessness must start with the realisation that air breathing is a recent development in evolution compared with other motor activities such as those of the heart or gut. When the need to pump air evolved, recourse was made to the striped "voluntary" muscles of the chest. The system of breathing we have evolved is as follows: the chemical state of the blood (particularly the P_{CO_2}) tells the lower brain (medulla) how much to breathe and the nervous input from the lungs probably tells the medulla how the lungs want to be breathed; that is, how deep and how fast. The medulla and neighbouring parts of the brainstem receiving these inputs then send instructions to the respiratory muscles. I have long thought that the sensation of breathlessness is generated not in the stimuli acting on the brainstem but in the nervous pathways controlling the respiratory muscles. I did not think this was a particularly pressing matter for research but after the symposium in Manchester described earlier I was often asked to talk about the subject. I became increasingly irritated by the many people who did not distinguish between afferent and sensory information; between what goes into the nervous system as opposed to what is sensed in the central nervous system.

* AE HOUSMAN, *A Shropshire Lad.*

One evening in the bar at Hammersmith it occurred to Stan Freedman, Tim Clark, and myself that we might test this idea by finding out what total respiratory paralysis does to the discomfort of breath holding. Everyone who has held his breath, and most of us have, knows that an uncomfortable sensation develops in the chest and that this becomes intolerable after a minute or so. Conventional wisdom was that this sensation was produced by the drives to breathe arising from the chemical changes in the blood and nervous stimuli from the lungs. According to my view though, the sensation probably arose in the breathing muscles or the nervous mechanisms driving them. If I were right, stopping the contraction of these muscles might abolish the sensation. Clinical observations in patients with respiratory paralysis were not, on the face of it, on my side in that these patients are breathless. I was pretty sure, however, that these patients would try to breathe and that inability to meet this effort would be distressing.

We were interested to discover if there is an unpleasant sensation like that of breath holding if one does not try to breathe so we decided to approach Gordon Robson, the professor of anaesthesia, to try to persuade him to curarise (to administer muscle relaxant to) one of us. Fortunately he was quite agreeable and together with Norman Jones and John Norman we formed a team. There was of course some discussion about who would be the subject but I insisted that it should be me. There were objections, however, largely based on the fact that I knew too much about the subject and might, albeit unconsciously, bias the findings. I argued that the major task lay in the performance of the experiment and that my experience would be very valuable in the detailed planning. If we did it successfully and safely on me then we would feel much happier about asking somebody else to volunteer.

In principle the experiment was quite simple. Firstly we would see how long I could hold my breath "normally", with all the apparatus and procedure set as they would be when I was curarised, and then repeat the whole performance when I was totally curarised. We could readily see how to overcome most of the technical problems of the experiment with one exception; how do you communicate with a totally paralysed subject? We decided to try and overcome this problem in the following way. The curare would be administered in single shots every few minutes. Before each shot, a blood pressure cuff around my arm would be blown up to above the arterial blood pressure and kept there for three minutes to stop blood going to the forearm and hand. During the three minutes, the curare would be taken up by muscles elswhere in the body leaving the muscles of that arm able to contract. This scheme worked; but only just! Enough curare got into the arm to paralyse the fingers completely, but I was able to muster flickers in the muscles around the wrist. Tim Clark's job was to watch the signal arm. Every ten to fifteen seconds he would ask a question to which the answer would be "yes" or "no". If the answer was "yes", I was to make two twitches; if "no", I was to make one twitch. Initially we were going to use the reverse, (one twitch "yes", two twitches "no") but when deeply curarised it was not always easy to manage two twitches and as our key repeated question was to be "Are you alright?", the inability to make two twitches could have been unfortunate.

So the rhythm was as follows:
"Are you all right?"
 Two twitches.
"Yes."
Ten seconds.
"Are you all right?"
Two twitches.
"Yes."
Note that Tim repeated my answer so that I could immediately twitch again if he had misunderstood me. We had agreed that immediately after one twitch (that is, "no") the next question would be "Do you wish to stop?". Two twitches would have been the signal to give me a general anaesthetic and bring me out of the paralysis in accord with usual anaesthetic practice. We also had a number of other

questions worked out, phrased in such a way that the answer would always be "yes" or "no".

We had a number of dry runs and then a dress rehearsal in which it was agreed that I would be fairly deeply curarised but without abolishing breathing. This "dress rehearsal" was very valuable because it showed how important it was to look after the positions of the limbs to stop them from being excruciatingly painful and to bandage the eyes to prevent a most uncomfortable double vision. It was during one of these dress rehearsals that I also realised the breath holding time was going to be prolonged but for how long dare we continue? We settled for four minutes because any longer period would be associated with various risks.

On the appointed day all went well. Gordon gave me the curare, John looked after my breathing, Stan and Norman looked after the physiological measurements, and Tim "kept in touch". When they had fully paralysed me I felt quite confortable. They then stopped ventilating me and the four minutes passed quite quickly as far as I was concerned but I understand it was the opposite for the others. We did it twice and then Gordon gave me something to reverse the paralysis. At this stage John stopped ventilating me but to his concern I didn't breathe so he restarted ventilation. Twice more he stopped and I didn't breathe. There was a muffled slightly tense discussion behind my head after which I heard Gordon's gentle Scottish voice in my ear: "Moran, would you mind trying to take a breath?" I did. No problem. I had been comfortable, leaving John to carry on breathing.

We repeated the experiment on Mark Noble without, of course, telling him what we had observed in me. In both of us curarisation had abolished the discomfort in the chest even though we were left without any breath for three times as long as we were able to hold our breath.

Thus my prejudice was supported; at least in breath holding. it would seem that the distress arises as a result of the efforts of the respiratory muscles to expand the chest.

All of us have a vivid memory of absolute quiet punctuated by the litany: "Are you all right?", twitch, twitch. The following passage by my namesake, Thomas Campbell (*Battle of the Baltic*) is perhaps rather an overstatement:

> There was silence deep as death,
> And the boldest held his breath
> For a time.

Where's McMaster? –
when "high" and "low"

Where's McMaster? – when "high" was written while mildly manic in 1978. *Where's McMaster? – when "low"* was written in 1982, having forgotten about the earlier version. The memory bank was, therefore, about the same.

McMaster – when "low" was written under duress. A psychiatrist suggested I try and break out of depression by shifting my biological clock. I was to go to bed at 8 or 9 pm and set the alarm for 3 am. Then I was to get up.

"What shall I do?"

"Write."

"What about?"

"Anything that occurs to you; yourself, if nothing else does."

And so I dragged myself from the only peace I knew, and after half an hour of fumbling with cups of tea and the stereo and a long period of just sitting I started the second version. I have included my marginal comments on my feelings and on the music that was my only companion.

I was cold, stiff, very tired, and very miserable.

WHERE'S McMASTER? – WHEN "HIGH"

In 1967, Centennial Year in Canada and Expo Year in Montreal, I was honoured to be asked to give the J Burns Amberson Lecture to the American Thoracic Society. This lecture, the highlight of the meeting of the most prestigious society in American chest medicine, is named after one of the greatest (and certainly the most loved) of American chest physicians who had been chief of the chest service at Bellevue

Hospital in New York. I was much younger than previous speakers and was also the first foreigner to be invited. I think the invitation was prompted by Carl Muschenheim, another very fine New York physician, who had been converted to my way of treating acute respiratory failure in patients with chronic, bad chests by controlled oxygen rather than by making holes in their windpipes and using machines to ventilate them. I gave the lecture to a packed house of some 2000 people in a hotel ballroom in Pittsburgh and took the opportunity not only to lay out the physiological reasoning but also to make caustic comments about "those who run intensive care units in which the treatment is more intense than careful". My platform style by this time was pretty good and although I certainly got the message across, I cannot claim a mass conversion. The intensivists were skeptical and even today the care in many American units leaves much to be desired. In fact, in the film *Hospital*, the scene is set by George C Scott's account of the rapid demise from respiratory failure of a patient whose treatment killed him even before he could be got into a hospital bed, thereby freeing that bed for the procreational activities of the intern. The lecture paid quite a handsome fee and I used some of the money to finance a quick tour across the States and up into Canada.

There, as on previous trips, I stopped off in Winnipeg to see Reuben Cherniack and Arnold Naimark. Reuben and Edy gave a party for me in their Scottish baronial mansion (prairie style). After most of the guests had left a hard core remained sitting around Edy's dining room holding "western" style conversation about the current number one topic; finding a new dean. In western style conversation the participants make seemingly casual but loaded remarks which, though apparently directed to one of the others, are really tossed into the ring to elicit an argument. These remarks and the responses are separated by long pauses – "wide open spaces" – to savour the innuendo and see who will rise.

After an hour or so the local heir apparent to the deanship left, the circle closed in, and the serious business began. The general mood was in favour of a strong dean. Winnipeg is a very fine school which, for its size, has produced more clinical scientists than any other in Canada. This record is due to the influence of a remarkable man called Joe Doupe (pronounced Dope). The school, however, has always been plagued by uneasy relations between itself and the very powerful clinics which dominate the medical life of the city. The conversation took the general line and only an insider can understand the problems of Winnipeg, to which the rejoinder was, of course, that if the problems are that bad, only an outsider can solve them.

One remark that produced some semblance of accord was, "Pity we didn't recruit John Evans." In the ensuing pause, intrigued by the uncharacteristic general enthusiasm, and never having heard of the man, I asked Reuben who he was. "A whiz kid young cardiologist from Toronto who is going as dean to McMaster."

"Where's McMaster?"

"It's a new school in Hamilton."

"Where's Hamilton?"

"A steel town near Toronto."

Somehow I formed an instant impression of John Evans. He was short, Welsh, quick witted, and probably an educational, "bull shit" artist who talked quicker than he thought. Having made up my mind on that point, I sat out the remainder of the conversation, forgot about McMaster, went to bed, and then on to Montreal for a day at Expo. This was great fun made all the better by having Giorgio Brandi as a companion. Giorgio comes from that marvellous physiology department in Milan which seems to breed exceptional men by having a genius as the chief and a financial system which permits survival of only the fittest. Giorgio's views on everything were much more refreshing than those of the rather stereotyped, energetic, young North Americans who tend to be long on research productivity and short on scientific thoughtfulness. The waits in the queues to enter the various pavilions were, therefore, made pleasurable by Giorgio's cynical but not unfriendly views on research, medicine, and all things American.

I then took the flight home. The best flight of all; little

sleep but the prospect of getting back to Diana, the kids, and giving them presents.

I gave not a thought to McMaster. Rumours filtered through to me that John E had some extraordinary ambitions, and that they were looking for staff, including a chairman of the department of medicine, but I, still thinking that Canada was much the same as the United States, took no notice until John Dickinson got involved. He had been a particularly successful visiting professor at McGill and was asked to visit McMaster. Early in January 1968 he combined a trip to his old stamping ground at Cleveland with a few days in Hamilton. On his return we had dinner – we were always seeing each other about our joint book as well as going to the theatre – and with a suppressed but definite sense of purpose he told me about his visit. He said they were searching hard for a chairman of medicine and his invitation to visit had been to sound him out about his interest in the job. He told me that it was not his cup of tea, but I ought to be considered and, for my part, if they approached me I should take the possibility seriously. Apparently, John E had already thought about me but had been advised not to touch me with a barge pole. The sum of the opinions he had apparently received about me was; "He's too awkward. With your town-gown problems, you would be asking for trouble".

I do not dispute that opinion. My behaviour has always been aggressive and my record as a candidate for professorships in the UK was disastrous. In my innocence, when asked at interviews for my ideas on medical education, I gave them. If I had had any sense, or if I had really wanted the jobs, I should have played it cool and given "acceptable", exciting sounding, but undisturbing answers. In fact, I usually proposed nothing more radical than had already been recommended by the leading thinkers about medical education in Britain. ("No country has produced more good reports on medical education and no country has done less about it.") I suspect, however, that the aggressive way in which I propounded my views put people off. I cannot swear to the following exchange though it certainly is representative of my views and my mode of expression at interviews. After I had thundered about the difference between education and training a professor of surgery asked me if I had no use for a sense of vocation, to which I replied that I valued the call of vocation immensely but preferred it to be answered by an educated man rather than by a knife-happy technician with a God complex. That's how not to win friends and any influence it has on committee people is unfavourable.

It appeared that John D had reassured John E that I wasn't as bad as all that and in January I received a letter asking if I would be interested in being considered for the post of chairman of the Department of Medicine at McMaster. Ten years later, my reply still seems to convey my response adequately.

"John D had warned me that you might approach me and he correctly indicated that I might be interested. My position and attitudes are as follows. I have got about as far as I can in my career and, while I am thoroughly enjoying myself, I am uncertain that I want to pursue the same line indefinitely. The only real promotion and the only real challenge would seem to me to become head of a department. In principle, I would rather work in a balanced medical community... In principle, I would rather form a new medical school than reform an old one. In principle, I would rather bring up my children in an expanding country than in a stable or contracting one. The problems come in practice. I and my family like London... Over to you."

John D had led me to understand that John E would be visiting London in the spring and I expected a reply to the effect that he would like to see me at the time. But no. One Thursday afternoon, about a week later, I was called from the lab to take a phone call from Canada. My memory of the start of this conversation is clear.

"John Evans here. Thank you for your letter. Glad to hear you are not entirely opposed to helping us out in the colonies. Could you come and spend two or three days here anytime in the next three months?" Fundamentally I regard the telephone as a sinful, costly machine and long distance telephone calls as extravagances only to be used in dire emergencies. A transatlantic call, even when I was not paying, concentrated my mind most wonderfully and when I put the receiver down I had agreed to fly over on Sunday.

I only remember two things about the next couple of days. John D came round and briefed me about the people I would meet and the places I would see. He was obviously concerned for himself, for McMaster, and for me that I should not "blow it" in my usual way. My other memory is of spending most of Saturday afternoon and evening putting up a curtain rail in the bedroom for some gorgeous, heavy curtains that Diana had made to replace the rotten, ten year old, cotton ones. I did not have a decent drill for the Black and Decker and had to use the old Rawlplug tool on some very hard brick. Then the drawstrings for the curtains almost defeated us; we had to put them on and take them off repeatedly to get the curtains to meet in the middle. I remember thinking, "Hell, you can't go to Canada after all this trouble." But the die was cast.

On Sunday I flew off to Toronto with a briefcase containing a novel, a shirt, underpants, pyjamas, and a razor. After going through customs I headed for the Hertz booth where John E had said we were to meet. There was only one person there and he was not short. In fact he was a rather gangly giant of about six feet six inches, attired in ski clothes. He was slightly surprised at my lack of luggage but hurried me off to a vast (to British eyes) station wagon with dozens of skis on the top and inside an all Canadian family – vivacious, beautiful wife and six uninhibited children. I was taken to a strange place with an Indian sounding name like the Tomahawk Club on "the mountain". This is the local name for the Niagara escarpment, which gives Hamilton its main physical character, squeezing it down to Lake Ontario and dictating its development.

John and his wife gave me dinner after which John took me back to the club where I was staying. This was rather eerie. It was the middle of winter and the club stood in its own grounds with the lights of Hamilton below. I was the only resident and the manager took pains, in a central European accent, to emphasise one thing. I must not attempt to alter the central heating in my room otherwise dire consequences might ensue. I slept two or three hours and then lay awake, partly because my biological clock was still six hours ahead and partly because of the heat and noise emanating from the ancient radiator. In the morning I found that the club was reminiscent of the sort of house the robber barons of New York have – built at the turn of the century, like the setting of *High Society*. My solitary breakfast was also eerie. The food was superb and I was attentively served by a German waiter in a manner which reminded me of the pre-war homosexual stories of Spender or Isherwood.

I was collected by John and driven down to the university where I was handed my schedule. John diffidently asked for my curriculum vitae, thereby revealing his familiarity with British attitudes as I had not thought to bring one. After all submitting a cv in Britain is tantamount to applying for a job. I pointed out pretty firmly that I had not applied for any job. He agreed that to ask for a cv was a bit presumptuous but pointed out that it would facilitate conversation with the people I was to meet. Truculently, therefore, I dictated a few salient facts to his secretary which she bashed out on a type-writer and sent off so that they arrived shortly before I did for my various appointments. I don't remember too much about the morning. I certainly met some able people who shared my concerns about education but who didn't persuade me that they were going to do anything exceptional and by the afternoon I was very depressed. I wondered how I could put up with another day of these repetitive, inconclusive, well intentioned chats and face the embarrassment of telling John that I was not interested. In fact on my way by taxi to one of the hospitals, through a particularly dreary part of the city, I had an overwhelming feeling of homesickness. I just wanted to go back to Diana by the first plane but as I didn't know how I went on with the schedule.

From then on things improved. I spent the late afternoon with Bill Goldberg, the chief of medicine at St Joseph's Hos-pital, then had dinner with Alan McNabb, his opposite number at the Hamilton Civic Hospitals, Although they were very different, and although most of our talk was inconse-quential, I realised that they were determined to make the medical school "go". The importance of this impression may be lost on those unfamiliar with North American hospitals who do not appreciate the power and influence of the "chief". I knew enough of the scene, however, to realise that with these men on my side my ineffable aims might be attainable. I say ineffable because although I was clear about my ends, I had no real idea about means whereas these men, although hazy about the ends, certainly controlled the means.

Later that evening came the crucial conversation with John E during which I threw every doubt and criticism I could at him. He evaded none. I particularly remember one exchange. In many cities in the States there are two or more medical schools, one of which is well known while the others are definitely second class. One assumes, until proved otherwise, that the students and staff are in the others because they are not good enough to make the best. Now only forty miles east of Hamilton lies Toronto, a highly respected if rather conservative medical centre. Choosing examples from the States I challenged John that despite all his good ideas we would just end up as the second best alternative to Toronto. He simply said that it was up to us.

I returned to the club but could not sleep. I paced the floor and drank a lot of the duty free whisky I had brought as a present to give to whoever seemed appropriate. Despite the warnings I tried turning off the radiator and thereby caused noises that resembled intestinal obstruction in a prehistoric monster. By the morning I realised that I had to take the place seriously. In the local vernacular, the time in my life had come when as a medical educator I had to "put up or shut up". Next day went well and when John drove me to the airport I was "high". We hurriedly laid plans to be implemented if, after a few days at home, I was still interested.

I managed a few hours sleep on the plane and was met at Heathrow by Norman Jones who drove me into Hammersmith. At this time Norman had almost reached the end of the line. We had managed to get money to give him something more than a senior registrar but no permanent appointment worthy of him was in view locally or anywhere else in the UK and I knew that he had had a firm offer of a good job in San Francisco. In a stilted way I tried to tell him that if I still felt the same in a few days' time my job at Hammersmith might be vacant and he should wait before accepting the offer in California. I think he said something to the effect that if McMaster was all that promising he would like to come too. I felt tears in my eyes. The next few days were very trying, particularly for Diana, as I could not come down from my high.

Some indication of my spirits is given in this passage from the letter I wrote to John E the day after getting back:

"My return fare was £171. 6s. od. and I enclose the counterfoil. I have no record of other expenses; the major items were chilled liquid sedatives on the flight home at 55 cents a shot. Although taken prn, the last dose I remember is the fourth."

After five days, I phoned John E at 3 am London time to say I would take the job if they would have me.

I had tried to look at the decision from the family point of view but my failure to do so was brought home to me a few days later when Diana and I were in a restaurant. I was babbling away when I suddenly noticed that she was crying – something she had only done about twice since I had known her. She apologised and said she stood by "our" decision but did I not realise what she would miss? Her parents, brothers and sister, and their children were all close to us, physically as well as in all other senses, and that side of life was very important to her. She tried to smile through the tears with some reference to the vows including "the worse" as well as "the better". (She has since told me that she knew from the tone of my voice when I called her on getting back to Hammersmith that we were going to Canada.) This episode brought me down with a bang and produced one of the moods of black depression – a feeling that I had made a terrible mistake – which recurred frequently until we moved to Canada, and not infrequently thereafter.

The next seven years stretched me to the limit and sometimes beyond and provided the material for many more reminiscences. At least to people interested in medical education, which in many ways is the ultimate challenge there is in education, there is now no uncertainty about "where's McMaster?" and what we stand for.

WHERE'S McMASTER? – WHEN "LOW"

Vivaldi – "Concerto for Violin and Guitar". Difficulty in thinking of what to write.

I think I first heard of the medical school at McMaster in Reuben Cherniack's sitting room in Winnipeg in May or June 1967. I was working my way round North America after giving the Burns Amberson Lecture. The talk in the room was about the search for a new dean in Winnipeg and somebody said, "We should have got John Evans." I asked who John Evans was and was told he was a whiz kid cardiologist from Toronto who was the dean of the new medical school at McMaster.

"Where's McMaster?"

"It's a university in Hamilton."

"Where's Hamilton?"

"It's an industrial city near Toronto."

I think I was also told McMaster was "revolutionary" but the vividness of this memory ends with a visualisation of John Evans as a fast talking, short Welshman whom I wouldn't like. So, I went on my way to Montreal, a day at Expo, and on home.

In December my good friend John Dickinson visited McMaster to look at the job of chairman of medicine. When he returned to London he told me he was not interested in the job but I ought to be. Later it transpired that my name had come up in discussion with John Evans who said he had been warned that I was "difficult". John D had contradicted his opinion and advised me that John E would be writing to me. The letter came in January. Quite a short letter asking me if I was interested. I replied briefly saying that the opportunity to start a new department in a new school in a new country had attractions over those jobs available in the UK but did not express much enthusiasm.

I hope I have these letters.

I suppose I expected another letter but instead, one Thursday afternoon in late January or early February, I was called from the lab to take a phone call from Canada. "John Evans speaking. Glad to hear you are not averse to helping us in the colonies. Can you come and visit us for a few days any time in the next few months?" I dislike long distance telephone calls, which frighten me because of their cost, and to cut the conversation short I agreed to go on the following Sunday. I flew over with just the minimum requirements in a briefcase and was met by John and his family at the airport.

I am compressing too much because I have not enough paper by me to last the night. And yet, there is typing paper and note paper somewhere around.

He and the family were very impressive in a New World sort of way. Station wagon with skis on top: all in ski clothes. They pointed out "the mountain" as we approached Hamilton. I had dinner in his home. I don't remember the talk but suppose we went over generalities and my schedule. (How often I was to do this in the next few years!) Then John took me to the Tamahaac Club. Bedroom very hot. Didn't sleep. The following morning I began a typical McMaster schedule of one hour talks. Vague flashes of memory of Zipursky (Paeds), Mueller (Surgery). Intense memory of depression and nausea on being driven through the town to St Joseph's but there things changed. Goldberg leaning back with feet on desk smoking a cigar. Obviously an effective man and committed to getting St Joseph's involved with the medical school. He walks me around the hospital. See crucifixes everywhere.

Duke Ellington. "Black and Tan Fantasy."

Ask if religion gets in the way of medicine. Goldberg says not.

"Don't Get Around Much Anymore."

I seize the opportunity to ask if religion obtrudes on everyday life, Irish background and all that. "Don't want to live in a Catholic/Protestant split community." Goldberg says "No. But why ask me? My name's Goldberg!"

Very tense. Am missing out much detail. Want to go back to bed. Must try to get back to Diana (in the memory). "Do Nothing 'til You Hear From Me".

Dinner with McNabb, Wilson, and Scime at the Hamilton Club – stuffy place. More evidence of community commitment to medical school but in retrospect realise that I talked too much about Hammersmith and not enough about Hamilton.

"A Train." Betty Roche singing – memories of last year's mania.

Cut short by John E who takes me home for a long talk. Very impressive. Back to Tamahaac. Manic. No sleep. Too hot. Walk up and down bedroom. Not much memory of next day. Manic. JE takes me to airport. Give him referees. Agree to return in March.

"Solitude"(!)

No sleep on plane. Damn it, I'm hooked. Met by Norman. "Don't take that job in San Francisco."

"Opus One."

"If I still feel the way I do, I'll be off to Canada and my job will be available."
"If it's as exciting a place as that, I'd like to come with you."

I think I wept.

Terrible manic day. Home to Diana. She has subsequently told me that she knew we were going to Canada as soon as she saw me. Continued manic. Sent telegram saying I wanted job. Few days later phone Evans about my visit in March. No longer so manic. He told me that senate had approved my appointment. Depression at thought of mistake. Swallow. "All right, I'll take it."

Took Diana out to dinner. I talk. She suddenly bursts into tears in the restaurant. Why? "It's all right for you, but think of what I'm giving up. Family. All the brothers, sisters, nephews, and nieces." Depression. (Didn't she say something about "for better or for worse"?)

No more clear memory until I go back to Canada. Go via few days in Baltimore to avoid jet lag. Snowstorm. Train from New York to Hamilton. No sleep. Vicious schedule in Hamilton. Stay in Evans's house. He goes away for spring break. See people all day. Dinners with VIPs like Mustard. Up until 2 to 3 am collecting thoughts, writing letters and notes. In to office at 6 am. After four to five days, take sedative and blow mind.

Ought to detail this. I really did become very, very high.

Evans comes back from holiday and chastises me. "Some of the best people are manic depressives." I remember him saying that, but impact did not sink in.

Gerry Mulligan.

Depressed. I've made a dreadful mistake. Try to talk to JE about how to undo the damage and get out of the job. He won't have any of it. Can't remember much more of visit. Was I high or low? (I have also forgotten my manic behaviour at Hammersmith on return from first visit. Sir John McMaster coming home to try and persuade me not to leave. Charles Fletcher saying he felt as though his right arm was being wrenched off.)

186

Don't like Mulligan. Change to Basie. "Five O'Clock in the Morning Blues" (sic). Actually, it's 5.20. Oh, how I want to go back to bed!

I think I must have been hypomanic all summer of 1968 because I got so much done. Took Diana to Hamilton in June. Little memory. She found university house, 111 Traymore Avenue. I was interviewing, planning, negotiating for teaching units at St Joseph's and Hamilton General. I can't remember much detail. (I had also forgotten from my first visit my photo tour of the town with Fred Johnson and seeing it at its worst, Barton and James in late March. Manic at the time and convinced myself easily that it was going to be a great place to live.)

One more visit in August. Also went to international Union of Physiologists Congress meeting in Washington. Quick visit to New York to interview Jack Hirsh. He said he couldn't come for two years. Then the move. All this time Diana had been wonderful and now she peaked. Quiet efficiency, and above all kept close to the kids and made the whole business seem natural. Very wet Sunday in London. Flew to Toronto. A few hours later having dinner in our new home. Steve Herbert, my administrative assistant, had fixed up all the appliances. (Also forgot that Saturday in June when Diana and I spent two thousand dollars in Eatons in less than a couple of hours.)

Remember a squabble with Diana when we went shopping and the kids were a nuisance. She pointed out to me that they were going through a difficult time and I must be more sympathetic. She always understands them better than I do. (Remember also "extravagant" shopping in London (Heals) before the move. Manic/extravagant *v* depressed/mean and so it goes.)

6 am. What use is all this? Why should I be concerned about its "use" – its value – because I want to be significant. Oh the Demon!

Last night Diana said, "Why are you so concerned about what people think of you? I'm not."

I think she has only wept two or three times since I have known her. I can remember once on our honeymoon when I was forcing intellectualism on her, implying she was poorly read. I wonder if she remembers. What would I do if she broke down under the present strain? My heart fills with love and shame when I think of her. She is my "centre": there must be a better word.

One evening in 1969 she said she was going to bed at about 9 pm. Expressed surprise. "This is the first evening in weeks that we haven't had somebody staying here or been entertaining or being entertained." I was shocked at the realisation of the strain I was giving her. Settling the family. Making a new home. Overwhelming hospitality. And all those recruits to be shown around the town. To use an obsolete English expression, she was "a brick".

Throughout my years as chairman, I think I worked on a weekly cycle. Hypomanic Tuesday and Wednesday. Manic Thursday and Friday. Depressed Sunday and Monday. I can remember several times when I collapsed – a "sack" went over my head and I slept deeply for twelve hours and awoke depressed.

This has gone nowhere and I have got to get dressed and face the day. Can I get myself to cycle in or will I give in and use the car?

Now I am tense. "Moping." How will I cope with Los Angeles? Too late to change my mind for the fourth time and not go.

6.45 am. More Vivaldi. Lie down on sofa.

So this is Hamilton–McMaster

As agreed with John Evans I went back to Hamilton in March 1968. For my part the original intention had been to have a longer, harder look at the job. Having been appointed, however, the purpose now was to get to grips with some of the problems that awaited the chairman of the department of medicine. They had such difficulty in finding the chairman that the list of problems was pretty long.

I flew back to Baltimore on Thursday and fulfilled a long standing wish to see Dick and the folks at Johns Hopkins again. In addition this arrangement would, I hoped, avoid the jet lag which had plagued me on the first visit. But the best laid plans.... There was a bad snowstorm the day I was due to fly from Baltimore to Toronto and I had to go by train. I stupidly travelled as cheaply as possible and had to sit up all night arriving in Hamilton rather the worse for wear.

I was immediately put to work interviewing possible candidates for key positions who had been specially brought to Hamilton to see me. The first I remember was a brilliant young Canadian neurologist now working in the States who, in principle, wanted to return to Canada but only to a job that guaranteed his ability to pursue his research. I had to restrict our interview to generalisations because, of course, I knew next to nothing about McMaster, Ontario, or Canada. In any event he decided to stay where he was and is now one of the top neurologists in the States. I wonder if he remembers our conversation and what part it played in his decision?

I saw him at 8.30 am, half an hour later than planned because of taking the train. Then I had a quick meeting with John Evans who outlined the schedule that had been arranged for the next few hours. He told me we were to talk over dinner at his house. The next morning he and his family were going for two weeks' skiing in Quebec, leaving me with his house, au pair girl, and car. It transpired that several other key people were also taking off because the third week in March is a school holiday in Ontario.

I found myself on a vicious treadmill. During the day I had hour long meetings with VIPs from the town and the gown. John also left me two one-foot piles of folders labelled "asap" and "if EJMC has time". These proved to be full of problems. Admittedly many of them were nice problems but to me they all seemed to call for prompt action. For the next few days my routine was as follows: 6 am to office to read files and dictate letters; 9 am to 6 pm interviews; 6 pm dine with one of my future colleagues and talk heatedly until 11 pm; midnight to 2 or 3 am collect my thoughts preparatory to dictating letters and memos next morning. Understandably the harder I worked the more I found to do; one problem would generate two or three more and the people I met always suggested others I should see "asap".

After two days I stopped sleeping altogether. Bill Walsh, the assistant dean, became worried about my behaviour and gave me two pills of a "good" sedative. That night I took both pills at 1 am and settled down. I must have drifted off because the next thing I knew was a blow on the head which was difficult to explain. Gradually I realised what had happened. The bed was against a wall and I had tried to leap out on my usual side, which happened to be the wall side. Gradually I pieced together where I was and thoughts began to chase each other through my head. Many of them were good thoughts which seemed to demand immediate action. I tried the bedside light but had difficulty in finding the switch. When I found it, the light didn't work and I remembered it was governed by another switch near the bedroom door. I climbed out of bed on the no-wall side and fell over. I lay there trying to work out the route to the door and eventually, on all fours, I found it and gingerly worked myself erect and found the switch. Still no light, so I groped to the bed and back to the door until both switches were on. Let there be light and after all this effort there was. Even then I found myself in a mess, staggering about picking up one thing after another while trying to get my thoughts in order. Must find some black coffee. Room at top of house and reached by a steep staircase. Fell down the staircase. Lie there in the dark wondering what to do next – go back to bed or struggle to the kitchen. Au pair girl appears in sexy peignoir, looks worried, and asks if I am all right ("not hurted"). Find it difficult to speak. Eventually see it is only 1.45 am. Two cups of coffee and I doze fitfully until dawn and then drive slowly to the university. Concentrate. Drive on the right. Remember this car is an automatic, so don't try to use the clutch because it is the (power assisted) brake. Make sure you have everything – especially keys. Concentrate. You really will be a brilliant and sucessful chairman but there's so much to be done – now, if not sooner.

And so to the weekend. On Sunday, very manic. Taken round the city and environs in the morning by dear Fred Johnson, the chairman of obstetrics and gynaecology (OBGY in Canada), and his wife, who wears an emerald green outfit. They are both Hamiltonians and show me where we may live – in big houses in places with big trees and snow banks. Take photos for the folks at home. Towards the end of the tour I protest that I have not seen the real Hamilton – the dirty steel city – so we drive through the steel mills and stop at the intersection of James and Barton. Grotty shops and cafés with drunks propping themselves against a wall. "So this is Hamilton. Yes we can live here." Sleep soundly that night and awake depressed. Run even faster on the treadmill next week and go high again. Decide to visit Montreal to see old friends and advisors, and some possible recruits. Behave badly – talkative, and aggressive. Maurice and Margot McGregor put me to bed, call John Evans, and put me on a plane on Sunday morning to be met at Toronto by John.

On the plane find myself talking to a passenger beside me. He turns out to be a professional wrestler.

"You know what I want to know?"

"Yes. Is it all fixed? No it isn't and don't you realise it would take more skill to act it up than to do it for real."

We discuss the anatomy and physiology of various holds

and I offer him an appointment in the department of anatomy as a "resource person" on functional anatomy.

Met by John who looks grim and makes his remark: "All the most productive people are manic depressives. The trick is to handle it so that you don't damage yourself or hurt others as you've been doing this past two weeks." Immediate depression and profound fatigue. Bounce up again and go home a week later.

On the last afternoon decide I should try and buy a house. Am given the name of a good realtor. Phone her.

"I believe you sell houses."

"Yes, what do you want?"

"A big house within bicycle range of the university."

"Difficult to come by, particularly at this time of year."

"You mean there aren't any."

"Well, only two or three."

"Is one of them better than the others?"

"Yes"

"I'll buy it."

Pause. "Would you like to see it?"

"Of course, but in view of what you tell me, it really isn't necessary."

"But I think you ought to see it. What will your wife say?"

"If you are as good at your job as they tell me, there isn't much she can say."

Pause. "Have you time to see it?"

"Yes, my plane doesn't go for another hour or so – I should be able to spare you ten minutes or so."

Pause. "I suggest you wait until you come back with your wife."

I did. We rented a university house. Three years and dozens of houses later, Diana told me she had found one that suited us.

"Buy it"

"Don't you want to see it?"

"Yes, but what effect will that have on our decision?'

Here we go again.

My war injury and its aftermath

In the late spring of 1944 I was a "combatant" at the ULSTC (University of London Senior Training Corps) undergoing intensive training at a camp on the escarpment near Berkhamstead and preparing for a heroic last ditch stand in defence of Churchill's bunker in Whitehall Strasse. We had travelled from Olympia in an unmarked train. As we were transferring from our personnel carrier (the No 27 bus) at the western end of Kensington High Street a little old lady approached us and asked:

"Excuse me. I'm sure it's a military secret but what are the ULSTC? I thought I knew most of our regiments but I have never heard of yours" she said pointing to the gold letters on the purple flash I had sewn on my shoulder. Lance-Corporal Viv, who resembled a teenage Telly Savalas, whispered to her, "Ultra-Light Specially Trained Commandos", his vowels and sibilants fighting and hissing through his clenched teeth. Sacret saiounds strite from Gowlders Grueen.

"Ooh! Are you going over there?"

"Can't say."

"No, I suppose you mustn't", she said and scurried off with her brown paper shopping bag to queue for her meat ration.

On the second Sunday at camp we had a break from manoeuvres and we Middlesex men challenged the St Mary's Hospital contingent to a game of coarse rugby. We knew that as "amateurs" we had no hope against the "professionals" of Praed Street. They had just beaten us for the fourth time running in the final of the Hospital Sevens and Nim Hall was playing for them at "out half" as Father called the position. I was playing in the second row, my usual position in the regular, extra-B team.

We had just conceded a scrum under our posts and Bill and I were giving an almighty shove to try and get the ball against the loose head when we were buzzed at tree top height by a yellow plane. In my scrum cap (improvised from a crepe bandage) with my ears occluded by the heaving bums of the front row, I heard nothing but suddenly, amid what seemed a crackle of machine gun fire, the scrum collapsed and I felt an acute pain at the base of my neck and down my left shoulder.

Since that injury I have a yearly recurrence of the pain and wake up about 4 am with a full blown torticollis (stiff neck) which may last several days. It is relieved by aspirin and gradually eases up during the day but wakes me in the early hours that aspirin cannot reach. Although sedatives plus aspirin may carry me through to 5 am, the symptoms are then worse because of my log-like immobility during the night. Furthermore I have a hangover from the sedative which makes it difficult to get out of bed and move around without falling over things. Herein lies my personal "Catch 22"; the choice between three hours sleep and some discomfort or six hours sleep and real pain. Usually I choose the lesser evil of insomnia because in addition to the pain at 6 am, I am incapacitated by the hangover from the sedative. I have tried all the medium and short acting non-barbiturate sedatives since the war (including thalidomide) but they don't work and I don't trust the newfangled long acting, "safe" analgesics.

In 1972 Helen, our statuesque Finnish-Canadian chief physiotherapist, and I had neighbouring offices as part of the advance party occupying the southwest corner of McMaster University Medical Centre (now called Mumsy) when I came in one morning with my neck all twisted.

"I'd love to get my hands on that neck", she said.

"My neck, no", I replied, "other parts, later."

I remembered her offer, however, and eight years later during a prolonged attack I put myself into the hands of Jenny, a wiry, little Indian physio whose manipulations and exercises returned my neck to its normal state. She, however, also revealed to me that because of my limited head rotation I had been unable to see that half of the world behind me visible to those with healthy necks. I now let Diana drive the car if there is much reversing to be done and have attached a rear view mirror to my sunglasses for use when cycling.

QUEEN VICTORIA'S BIRTHDAY, 1980

In 1980, I had a particularly vicious and prolonged bout of neck ache and torticollis brought on by heaving the water pump into position under the deck of the cottage during the annual May 24th celebration of Queen Victoria's birthday. All Canadians know this ritual of "opening up the cottage" after the breakup of ice on the lakes (the lesser ones, the Great Lakes do not freeze).

One morning about 7 am, bored with insomnia and fearful of waking the family as I pottered around the cottage, I decided to go into Sprucedale in search of plastic drainage tubing, taps, and other connections with which to construct a winterised water system to avoid the cold water and black flies of the Victoria weekend ritual and the carrying of buckets up from the water hole we had cut in the lake when here at "New Year's."

Sprucedale (population uncertain, but about two hundred) is a pleasant little place on an abandoned logging railway (railroad in the States; railway in Canada) to the west of Bear Lake. Businesses open at about 10 am but never close, even on Boxing Day (observed in Canada but not in the States: another example of the way Canada benefits from its bicultural English and Scottish heritage) when the local garage man will come out with his four wheel drive and start a frozen engine at the standard charge. On three occasions I have been hauled out of ditches by passing locals driving trucks who won't take a tip even if it's "for a drink at New Year's".

On the morning in question, after getting most of what I needed at the local general store, I was sipping a root beer for breakfast. Root beer is a byproduct of the unfortunate side of our Scottish heritage. "The Scotch", as Galbraith, one of their most distinguished sons, described in his little auto-biography, introduced that tedious combination of public puritanism and private alcoholism which expresses itself in the appalling privation of the local liquor laws and scarcity of good wine.

I found the root beer marginally less nauseating and flatu-lent than the Cokes and pops and was having my second can as I ambled around the heart of downtown Sprucedale when I came across what used to be a private garage outside which were a brand new water heater, a rusty Land Rover minus wheels, and a disemboweled rusty Chrysler slant-six motor. These were festooned with odds and ends of lengths of tubing and wires like plastic pasta. Inside I could see piles of junk of every sort.

Uncertain whether this was the harem of a service man or of a wild industrial archeologist, I tentatively approached the front door of the house nearest the collection of twentieth century artefacts. On the door was a name in four inch capitals: ED SOPER. Later I asked Ed if he was related to Lord Soper.

"Never heard of him. Is he rich – I'll write to him."

"Poor as a church mouse", I quipped.

The size of the lettering suggested that the words were meant to convey some business activity but gave no other clue. The screen on the front door was shut but the door was open. There was no bell, so I knocked. No response. I opened the screen door and slowly advanced, knocking on the wood-work with increasing force until I was in the kitchen end of the living area. Everything was spotless and tidy; the contrast with the garage should have alerted me that this was not the home of a wild loner.

Still no response.

"Anyone at home?"

From round a curtain on the right came a muffled grunt. "Cummin" was what I heard, but five minutes later as I waited outside, it turned out that Ed had really said "Cum in."

By now, ignoring the evidence of the kitchen, I had a firm hypothesis that this was the home of a solitary alcoholic. The hypothesis gained corroboration when a plethoric, round faced, stubby, late middle aged man shuffled out on the porch and said nothing but beckoned, nay summoned, me into the kitchen. He plonked himself down in front of the cornflakes and cold coffee and thrust his forefinger across the table towards another chair; a gesture which I took to mean "sit down".

At this juncture I cannot say that my first hypothesis was abandoned but it was rapidly joined by another: "severe, chronic airflow obstruction, probably on steroids". This hypothesis was soon sustained and the first one refuted by the twinkle in the blue eyes and the quick fire of the opening rounds in our conversation.

"What are you looking for?"

The thing I most wanted was a one and a quarter inch auger bit to drill a hole for the piping through the four by eight beams supporting the floor of the cottage. I had just refused to pay $8.44 for a one inch bit at the general store. Initially the owner had estimated its price as $4. He whistled when he looked it up in the catalogue. "I wouldn't sell you that. Probably too small anyways."

The patient across the table, when told what I thought I was seeking shook his head.

"You don't want to buy a one and a quarter inch bit." Wheeze. "You want to borrow an expanding bit."

Pause. "Don't sell a man a thing." Wheeze. "Study his problem."

Momentarily I was taken aback but fascinated by the blue eyes and the sharpness facing me. I decided to go for the jugular and to hell with professional etiquette.

"Where's your Ventolin?"

Slight puzzlement clouded the twinkle. A nod to the kitchen dresser.

On it I found three canisters of inhaler – one of Ventolin and two of other brands.

"I'll show you how to use it."

"I know."

197

"No you don't. Even if you follow directions. They're wrong."

So I then went through the sequence carefully developed by a quarter century of experience of showing patients how to use a nebulised inhaler.

More puzzlement.

"Who are you anyway?"

"Canada's number one chest specialist." (A slight overstatement but, after all, I was immediate past president of the Canadian Thoracic Society.)

While waiting for the salbutamol to work I "took a history" including questioning the patient thoroughly about current medications. This enquiry produced a nod slightly upwards in the direction of the cupboard in the dresser. On opening this, in marked contrast with the state of the garage outside, were standing serried ranks of pill containers covering the full range of polypharmacy which patients with bad chests now get theophylline, sodium chromoglycate, digitalis, diuretics, slow-K, antibiotics, and some "nerve pills for sleeping" which I couldn't recognise. Even at the back, in an unlabelled screw top bottle, some good old ephedrine, or so I guessed from their small size and bitter taste. The only items missing which would certainly be found in similar surroundings in continental Europe were suppositories.

We were now joined by Ed's wife whose appearance immediately explained the discrepancy between the neatness of the kitchen and the chaos of the garage.

The essentials of their life story emerged. He was born in Rugby. "But I didn't go to school there", he twinkled. She was born in Blackburn. The syllables were pronounced in unmistakable Gracie Fields' fashion despite sixty four years in Canada. They had come over in 1913, he, age nine, in the Teutonic from Liverpool ("Not to be confused with the Titanic") and she, age eight, on a cattle boat from Manchester. They had later met at Dufferin and Eglinton in Toronto. He had been a hard rock miner ("But no silicosis, just in case it crosses your mind."). During the war he had worked on construction at Gander and other northern airfields. In the late 'fifties and early 'sixties he had worked on the DEW line and had crossed the Arctic.

The conversation shot off in other directions. Mention of the Titanic led to the wonder of Brunel and the Great Eastern. Although he knew a great deal about the vessel, he didn't know it had to be launched sideways at Millwall. ("Thought it was built on the Clyde." Wheeze. "Would have been launched arseways there.") Mention of having electricity in the cottage led to "Egyptians may have discovered it." Wheeze. "Those paintings in the pyramids." Wheeze. "Couldn't have used oil lamps."

Without putting him down I said he must mean the tombs in the Valley of the Kings and was about to suggest another explanation of the way the artists may have illuminated the walls when he interrupted me. "Could have used mirrors." Wheeze. "But they would have to be damn well made", wheeze, "and damn well focussed", wheeze, "to get enough light round all those corners."

Eventually I brought the conversation back to my need for an expansion bit.

He would lend me his.

"Where is it?"

By now I thought his breathing was easier and seeking acknowledgement of my skill I asked.

"No better – but then, no worse", wheeze, "from your ministration."

Twinkle, twinkle. A nod to the garage. "Now follow my instructions", wheeze, "carefully". "On the right", wheeze, "inside the door is a bench." Wheeze. "On the bench at the right hand end, nearest the door, is a vice." Two wheezes. "Find the vice and at the left hand end of the bench at or about the level of the vice you will find the bit." (All that without stopping – salbutamol must be working.) "But be careful. It may be pointing up."

The need for such precision escaped me until I attempted to follow the directions. The bench was about eight feet long and was covered inches deep in a pile of small and medium size objects which at the left rose to a veritable compost heap of metal much higher than the vice. The location of the bit now being determined, I was at a loss how to excavate it. There was nowhere to put the contents of the mound above it.

By now he had shuffled on to his front porch but was too breathless to come over to the garage. So I called,

"But where shall I put all the other things."

"Just", wheeze, "misplace them", wheeze, "somewhere else. And", wheeze, "when you find it", wheeze, "let me know", wheeze – "in Greek."

Two or three minutes later my finger felt the twin little cutting edges of an expansion bit and I shouted The Word.

Intensity

The first part of this piece, looking at intensive care from the standpoint of a doctor, was written while I was slightly manic. Initially I intended to submit it to one of the general medical journals but decided against that because it was too long and they would have required me to take out the colour and the human interest. I then thought about sending it to some widely read periodical which occasionally publishes articles of medical interest such as *The New Yorker* or *Playboy*. I had sufficient insight to doubt my judgement, however, and passed it, for comment to some colleagues, most of whom said, "sit on it". A few, braver souls said "Publish". (They didn't say anything about perish.) Naturally, as I did not wish to discredit myself or my colleagues, I went with the majority. Any decision was forestalled by a return of depression which lasted until the following summer when, as recounted in the second part, I experienced intensive care from the other side of the bedclothes. The road accident (see later), which did so much damage to Diana, was probably due to mania: it always causes problems with my sleep. During the most stormy parts of Diana's stay in hospital I deteriorated. My behaviour became too manic for the children to cope with and I had to go into hospital myself at which time I wrote this part from the standpoint of the patient and relative.

I have revised both the original manuscripts in an attempt to lessen the gratuitous offensiveness of some of the writing without obliterating my thoughts and feelings at the times.

We had returned from the cottage late in August, partly to let one of my colleagues get away for an extended Labour Day holiday but chiefly to clear the desk before the post-Labour Day rush. In particular, I wanted to have a final look at our grant applications. Just before going to bed on the evening of the 28th, I was called about a patient by a very able young internist. From what he said I realised that I would have to go in and see the patient. He was a solitary man of seventy nine who had been blind since the age of seventy and had been admitted to hospital two days before because he was "bringing up blood". I say "bringing up blood" because there had been some uncertainty about its source. It seemed pretty obvious to me that it was coming from somewhere above the oesophagus and the larynx. The cause was unknown but the immediate threat to life came not so much from drowning in his own blood or respiratory failure caused by aspiration of blood into the lungs but from loss of blood. The day after admission there was a bleed measuring one litre in the aspiration bottle.

The urgency of this patient's admission had caused him to be transferred from one unit and one person to another so that nobody had decided how officiously we should strive to keep this lonely man alive. The young internist and I were faced with the need to deal with him simply as a technical problem.

As I was going through his chart and talking about him with the internist, who was on call for the intensive care unit (ICU), I noticed out of the corner of my eye that the patient was suffering some "episode" superficially suggestive of "aspiration". The resident was treating the patient with a sense of urgency, though in a style which to me was reminiscent of an infuriated plumber faced with a blocked sewer. I went across and had a quick listen to the back of the chest and heard good breathing sounds and no wheezes or crackles. It was this episode which drove me to the conclusion that his distress was due to something unpleasant in the larynx rather than in the lungs. The several streams of information I had picked up led me to the following partial conclusions: bleeding from the upper respiratory tract or from the throat, probably venous; query a benign growth; query, has the blindness anything to do with it?

That listing may seem to be the result of some logical process but these and other possibilities were pursuing roller coaster, parallel paths in my mind and to say the formulation was reached logically would be to lie.

Obeying my implicit brief of a glorified technologist, required to keep the patient alive, I followed up the hunch that he might have a benign lesion in his upper respiratory or gastrointestinal tract. This did not seem very likely but since the disappearance of tuberculosis, profuse bleeding from the respiratory tract, unaccompanied by other symptoms, must raise the suspicion of a treatable cause. The second hunch was that his blindness might be a clue. Somebody, somewhere in the notes, had suggested that it might have been due to temporal arteritis (an inflammation which affects the arteries to the optic nerves as well as the arteries in the temple). The nine year gap seemed to make that unlikely. I was told by the resident that he had been given to understand that the blindness was adequately explained on ocular grounds and that an ear, nose, and throat surgeon had said that there was nothing in the pharynx or thereabouts. On pursuing this "understanding" still further, however, by telephoning the ophthalmologist and the otorhinolaryngologist, I found that neither had seen the patient.

There was no immediate threat to life at this stage provided his upper airway was properly cared for and blood was available for transfusion. I instructed the residents and nurses in the gentle art of sucking blood out of a pharynx which may contain a bleeding vessel and showed them how to use an endotracheal tube in such a way that the pressure prevents the leakage of air but allows blood to flow into the lining of the airway. The bleeding did not recur for the next few days. The patient was found to have a carcinoma at the bifurcation of the trachea, so my hunch was wrong and my tube was not to be credited with staunching the bleeding. I'm embarrassed to say that I do not know what eventually happened to him.

Next day I cleared the desk and had a good night's sleep but woke early and lay thinking about the blind man and three other patients I had "inherited" when I came on call for respirology. One of these was a lady with chronic airflow obstruction suffering (literally) from a tracheotomy. A quick look through her chart and an examination of her chest did not persuade me that the tracheotomy had ever really been needed but she was now stuck with it and was being well cared for by one of my colleagues. The state of the patient was stable so I did not interfere.

The second patient was a fifty year old man estranged from his wife. He had very bad airway obstruction, though even when he was said to have been well, a year previously, his breathing capacity had been twenty per cent of normal. He had a large mass in the centre of the right lung, large hard lymph glands above his collarbone, and malignant cells in his sputum. He obviously had lung cancer which was both advanced and inoperable. After bronchoscopy, the purpose of which was unclear to me, he had suffered a cardiorespiratory episode. The nature of the episode was unclear to the resident now on duty and also uncertain from the chart but was said to have "necessitated" tracheostomy. I wanted to get the tube out because I thought it had done its immediate job, whatever that might have been, and from now on it was going to be doing increasing harm. I saw the patient's estranged wife to explain the position. She was distraught and insisted that everything possible should be done for her husband (probably out of guilt rather than affection). She left me in no doubt that should he deteriorate after I removed the tube I might be in trouble. I learned that she had a brother coming in that Saturday from a neighbouring town so I arranged to see the pair of them later. To cut a long story short, by working with and through the brother over a series of conversations, I got them to see the problem in better perspective and agree to removal of the tube. This was carried out uneventfully.

The third patient was in some ways the most distressing of all. She was the seventy five year old wife of an eighty year old, deaf Welshman. They had been married for fifty years and despite living in Canada for thirty five of those years, their speech was pure north Welsh. In the last month she had developed some nasty general condition in the lung which had been energetically treated for all possible infections but she was deteriorating and now had an endotracheal tube which she disliked intensely. Her husband was refusing to visit her in the ICU because he could not stand the sight of her there and because they could not talk. The junior staff were reluctant to remove the tube because it was felt that the mechanical ventilation was needed to buy time while hoping that steroids, which had recently been started, might take effect. I did not think that the intubation was needed and was not persuaded that it was doing more good than harm. I decided to take it out provided the family appreciated the risk. Fortunately the couple had a very sensible daughter to whom I put my case, emphasising the risks.

Like so much of desperate medicine this story had its funny moment. When people are semiconscious they will often respond to their native tongue. In any case to speak to them in their own language is to come closer to them as human beings. I whispered in her ear something that sounded like "tookladeen" which I thought was a Welsh term of endearment.

She could not, of course, speak but smiled and I felt both proud and encouraged. I recounted this little episode to the daughter who, having grown up in Canada, did not have the Welsh. She in turn told the old man in a very loud voice. When she came to "tookladeen", the old man looked very puzzled, leant even closer and cupped his hand to his ear. I thought it must be my pronunciation. At that instant I was called back by a nurse to check an order. When I returned everyone was laughing. His daughter then translated, "tookladeen means asshole." It must have been a term I learned from a Welsh rugby forward rather than from a Welsh pub barmaid.

We took the tube out uneventfully and she died gracefully

205

three days later, talking in Welsh with her husband almost to the end. He subsequently sent me a paperback of rugger songs.

So I spent that weekend on call as "respirologist" for the ICU trying to introduce a greater humanity into the overall management of these patients while at the same time lessening the intensity of the care to which they were being subjected. This experience and others like it prompted me to try and put on record my thoughts about ICUs and "intensivists" (or whatever they like to call themselves). I have been in and out of this field for some thirty years. It is on the whole a young man's game but I feel that someone of my age should be prepared to stand up and ask some questions. I recognise the risk in doing so because one will be accused of being "in favour of death", which may be an even worse sin than being "against motherhood".

I am sure there is no need to detail the immense cost of this branch of medicine which now calls itself "critical care medicine" but which I assert is by no means characterised by "critical" in the wider sense. It has its meetings at which the tangible manifestations of the industrial-medical complex remind one of the industrial-military complex; it is spawning paramedical professions; it is all very, very expensive even if we count the cost in money alone.

In the United Kingdom the growth of ICUs was not quite so rapid as in North America, partly because of limitations of money and partly because of the persistence of old hospitals in which the Nightingale wards permit better nursing. In North America many factors have combined to encourage or at least permit the growth of ICUs. Firstly increasing technology means that nurses have to spend more of their time tending to the paraphernalia around the patient rather than the patient himself. Secondly the hotel corridor type of private hospital ward which developed all over America in the 'forties and 'fifties makes big demands on the nursing staff. Any nurse leaving the nursing station to attend to a patient is bound to worry in case somebody in one of the other rooms pushes a button while she is away. Furthermore the whole business of communicating by button pushing is unsatisfactory to both parties; the nurse does not know how serious the call is and the patient does not know how long he or she is going to have to wait. Thirdly the force of the industrial-medical pressure groups is greater in North America. Fourthly, and perhaps most in the public eye, the medico-legal implications of letting a patient die or leaving no stone unturned are too worrisome to contemplate, particularly for a junior doctor or for somebody who is simply a "consultant" rather than the doctor in overall charge of the patient (as was my position). Herein lies a further twist in the vicious spiral; the more complicated the treatment of these patients becomes the less any single individual behaves as a proper doctor and the more he behaves as a technician.

All this might not be too bad if the problem of the true costs of intensive care did not have ramifications. These units are very, very expensive and lead to the paradox that the larger they are, the larger the slice of the hospital's pie they consume, and the worse the care elsewhere in the hospital. This leads to the "yo-yo" treatment in which a patient has become fit enough to be discharged from the ICU (often because someone with more clout wants the bed) and then a few days later has to be put back in the ICU because the Holiday Inn type of facilities of the ordinary ward cannot cope.

What evidence have we got about the cost/benefit of all this? Precious little, and none of it remotely showing either effectiveness or efficiency in a manner that would be acceptable to Archie Cochrane. There are some clues, however, pointing to the fact that if we look for evidence of "outcome/benefit" rather than transient, beneficial effects there is not much to go on. A few years ago Griner showed that the only effect of intensive care on the management of patients with left ventricular failure or pulmonary oedema in a leading American university hospital had been to increase the cost of treatment. Some time ago I had the temerity to suggest that the mortality of patients admitted to some American hospitals with acute or chronic respiratory failure who were treated in the standard American way was compatible with the hypothesis that the patients fell into two populations: those who died because of the treatment and those who survived despite it. The relative longevity of the survivors of this treatment, therefore, was really a sort of Darwinian tribute to their resilience.

In the absence of critically acceptable studies I am reduced to offering my impression, based upon many visits to many ICUs. I conclude that few of the patients with respiratory disease treated in ICUs in North America are there because they need to be. They are there because the health care system has failed them, not because the natural history of their disease requires them to be.

Perhaps I can put my case in the form of an anecdote. About twenty years ago I introduced a method for treating acute on chronic respiratory failure, based upon control of the oxygen concentration the patient breathes with a novel mask coupled with close nursing attention (see *Controlling Oxygen*). When showing this mask to an expert in an ICU in the mid-West, the following dialogue ensued.

Expert, with disdainful look at mask, "What happens if it falls off?"

Me, "What happens if one of the patients in your ICU pulls out his tracheotomy tube?"

Expert, "The nurse will put it back."

Me, "Conclusion: in your hosital first get your throat cut then call your nurse."

On the same trip I appeared on a panel with one of America's leading experts, who told the assembled multitude, most of whom practiced in non-university hospitals, that in respiratory failure the monitoring of respiratory failure by blood gases is mandatory. In the privacy of the bar, however, he subsequently admitted that, except in his own unit, the blood gas measurements were not to be trusted in any hospital in his city. Of course blood gases are now easier to measure reliably but the principle of forcing technology, even when it is not yet fit, remains. We had great difficulty in finding a journal to publish the study in which we found that a quarter of the residents and interns in a good hospital might have given inadequate care had their interpretations of blood gas measurements dictated practice. Fortunately, however, few therapeutic misadventures in fact occurred, largely because no notice was taken of the results of the blood gas analyses. The house staff was simply ordering them as part of the routine tests.

What of "life" in the units themselves? For many patients it must be like entering Hell before they are dead. It is well known that sleep deprivation is a good way of destroying the personality. The turnover of staff in many units is testament to the strain on them. One has either to have a superb mental balance or very bad mental balance to work for long in an ICU; most of us have neither. Then there is the bizarre situation that in many hospitals ICU duty is added to other responsibilities so that a member of staff may have to work night and day. It is like an airline which boasts that it is so successful and busy that the flight staff have had insufficient sleep to take off or land safely.

The late Henry Miller asked me to chair a working party for the British Medical Association on ICUs (intensive treatment units as they are called in the UK). When I disclaimed my suitability on the grounds that I had worked in a hospital without one (that is, the Hammersmith Hospital), he said characteristically that that made me all the more suitable for the job. I soon realised that the central problem in running an ICU is *responsibility*. There is a big difference between the consolidation of resources in a small or moderate sized hospital, where there is intimacy between the staff and meeting the needs of very large, highly specialised hospitals. In the former there is usually little difficulty, whether formally or informally, in deciding who is in charge of a patient. In the latter, despite all manner of rules, there is always equivocation about whether the ultimate responsibility lies with the admitting physician, the man running the ICU, or some other consultant. In any case most of the care is actually given by the house staff and which of them, in these days of litigation is going to say that he is embarked on a fruitless and inhumane technical exercise or take the trouble to suggest how better care of the patient, either before admission to hospital or elsewhere in the hospital, might have avoided the need for the ICU?

Then the final irony sank home. In most hospitals the combination of moral cowardice and technical incompetence is the best (or "least bad") the patient can expect. The moral cowardice about allowing a patient to die is in a few days or hours cancelled by the technical incompetence of the efforts to keep him alive, so that the net effect is to postpone (often not unduly) passage to that "undiscovered country from whose bourn no traveller returns". Would that some could return to advise us. Certainly there are occasional reported episodes of recovery from cardiac arrest to show that some effort is worthwhile but how many uncommunicative but perhaps sentient vegetables with broken ribs, torn livers, tracheostomies, and tubes everywhere do we have to put in the counterbalance? Furthermore for every one of these reports of "success" there is a long list of unpublished, nay unpublishable, anecdotes of accidents of misdiagnosis, analytical errors, failure of transmission of information, etc.

The worst combination, however, is moral cowardice coupled with technical competence which produces the spectacular "who will switch off the ventilator?" situation from which only lawyers profit.

Enough. The tide is washing over me.

OCTOBER 1982

I put the foregoing polemic away in a drawer. In addition to the reasons I gave at the start of this piece, I was also swayed by the wish not to hurt the many nurses and doctors who had done their best for the patients I describe. Nor could I bring myself to face the hassle of fighting editors who would be advised by "peers" representing powerful lobbies. In the past six weeks however, my wife and I have been consumers of the system and my passion, far from being lessened by having our lives saved, has been greatly increased. Between us we have been in four ICUs and two coronary care units. The circumstances were as follows.

On the night of 6th/7th August, while mildly manic, I worked far into the night on my grant application for which the deadline was the end of the month. In the morning Diana and I saw the realtor and arranged to buy a smaller house and then about noon we set off for the cottage which is about four hours drive north. We agreed that Diana should drive because of my bad night and because I have a tendency to go to sleep on long journeys. About halfway, Diana herself complained of sleepiness and stiffness and asked me if I would mind taking over. I reluctantly agreed.

That is the last thing I remember and the events of the next hour are reconstructed largely from the testimony of the very nice policeman who arrived on the scene five minutes after the accident. Apparently we drifted off the road on a gentle, left hand turn, sideswiped two parked vehicles (expensive), and came to rest with the right front end on a large piece of rock. The right front wheel was just in front of the passenger seat. None of the dozen bottles of wine in the trunk was broken and the skid marks were trivial. Diana had a bad bang above her left eye and was still in her seat moaning, "I think my back has gone." Apparently I was kneeling beside her examining her legs and insisting that she should not be moved until an ambulance arrived. I had a badly lacerated wound on my left temple but otherwise seemed to be well. It would seem that I had drifted off to sleep and the car off the road. On hitting the rock, Diana had been thrown forward, rotated around the diagonal band of her seatbelt, and struck her head on the windscreen. I seemed to have been thrown straight forward, hitting my head on the sun visor, but was saved from an abdominal or chest injury by the seatbelt. All in all, thank God that the MG has a chassis and that we were wearing seatbelts.

My memory returned on the forty five minute drive to the nearest hospital in the small town of Parry Sound and I found myself examining Diana's legs and feet. She could move her feet after a fashion but there was loss of sensation in the lumbar region.

We were promptly and well looked after in the hospital. To cut the story short, they found that I had no bony injury but that Diana had broken some ribs on the right, had a fracture dislocation of the twelfth thoracic vertebra with gross displacement, foot drop, and loss of sensation in the lumbar region (L four to five).

The surgeon decided that the problems were sufficiently severe to require transfer to a major trauma centre in Toronto, whence we were flown by helicopter and admitted at 8 pm, some four hours after the accident. Before we left the admirable young policeman volunteered to look after our dog but apologetically relieved me of one hundred and twenty eight dollars for careless driving. Quite right too!

Diana's case has subsequently been horrendously complicated so to save space I shall recount it telegraphically.

On admission. Excellent assessment clearly related to me by a neurosurgeon who looked like Steve McQueen. Said he was calling in general surgery for the belly and orthopaedic surgery for the back. An hour later the general surgeon (Marcello Mastroiano) gives me a very clear picture of the position and what he intends to do. Shortly later, equally impressive interview with the orthopaedic surgeon (JPR Williams).

10 pm. To surgery. First the belly. A lot of blood and a clot the size of a grapefruit in the pancreas cleaned out, and a drain inserted leading out onto the abdominal wall.

Midnight. Turn her over and put the twelfth thoracic vertebra back in place quite easily. Secure it with two rods and graft the broken bones with some chips. Inspect the spinal cord without opening the coverings. Looks OK. Anaesthetist puts tube into right side of chest without, either then or subsequently, adequate justification.

4 am. To Neurology ICU.

6 am. Comes round and seems to be in good shape.

First week after operation. As comfortable as can be expected after such a filleting and the six tubes here and there. Most misery from dangerous chest tube. Eventually after strong hints from me, the anaesthetist (Gore Vidal) reluctantly removes it with dramatic benefit. Gut must be at complete rest so nutritional team (headed by Harry Belafonte) gives some concentrated goo into one of the great veins near the heart.

Second week. Not so good. Fever of unknown origin. Infectious disease team (led by Diane Keaton) play roulette with antibiotics while waiting for some abscess in the belly to declare itself.

Third week. Very worrying. Fever 40° C and no cause found.

End of week. An abscess the size of a golf ball found near the gall bladder. Two hour exploration and drainage of said abscess. Nothing else to be found anywhere.

Improved for two days and then dramatic deterioration. Goes completely mad (toxic confusional psychosis). It takes me and three nurses half an hour to persuade her to have her temperature taken. Accuses me of trying to kill her. Temperature 41° C, pulse 180, blood pressure 50. Toxic shock.

Midnight 25 August. Told that she will not last the night. Seen by brilliant and brave surgeon (Christopher Plummer).

5 am. Phones to say he found what he had expected, an abscess like a six inch Polish sausage hiding behind the wreck of the pancreas. Cleared it out and put in yet another drain to the body surface.

Next morning. No fever. Rational.

Subsequently. Minor fevers due to infected intravenous lines, the last of which comes out nine weeks after the accident (and after her last meal).

All this time Diana had jaundice and double vision neither of which were ever adequately explained.

RESPONSIBILITY AND COMMUNICATION

The care Diana received was exemplary but at no time, until I insisted, did anyone assume overall command. The role was then well played by the chief of surgery (Henry Fonda). Up until that time it was played ad hoc by whoever had most of the action at the time.

I was never called and told exactly what was happening by anyone – neither by staff, residents, nor nurses. One Sunday I calculated that to get an overall picture of what was going on, I would have to quiz fourteen residents and of course that would be futile because three quarters of them were only on call.

I had to spend many hours in waiting rooms with other relatives. They were uniformly grateful for the quality of care being received by their relatives but, on inquiry, all professed ignorance about what was happening to their loved ones. They had an occasional word from nurses but otherwise doctors only spoke to them at moments of high drama and then it was almost always a different doctor from the last one to speak to them.

At the time of writing, Diana is well. Her double vision has inexplicably gone. Her drips are all out. She has only two drains in her belly. She is eating but has forgotten the taste of food and champagne tastes like Pepsi (not, unfortunately, vice versa). Her bowels are working three times a day and contain no undigested food so her pancreas seems to be working. Her jaundice is diminishing and her haemoglobin concentration is rising. She has gained ten pounds in ten days and lies beautifully in bed. Her voice and her mind are as clear as bells. Above all, she is walking by herself, admittedly with two canes. Her homecoming will be delayed four weeks by a fungus which has spread all over her body and can be seen in her retinae.

MY OWN CASE

My own case was pallid by comparison.

Midday, 14 August. Walking down Yonge Street get pain in chest and upper jaws. Breathless. Have to stop every fifty yards. One hour bus ride home felt like death; literally felt I was dying. Go to hospital.

Seen by nurse-practitioner (Jane Fonda) who takes excellent medical history, does a physical examination and electrocardiogram and in ten minutes, diagnoses myocardial ischaemia.

Followed by medical resident (Lynn Redgrave) who flaps around for half an hour and gets it all wrong.

Seen by accident officer (Humphrey Bogart) who takes twenty minutes to confirm the obvious.

Seen by medical student (Deborah Kerr circa 1950) who was too shy to get anywhere in thirty minutes.

Seen by family doctor (Robert Young) who takes five minutes to check out Jane and calls an internist (Marlon Brando) who does a thorough and largely unnecessary examination, probably because of the patient's identity.

And so on to full electrocardiogram by Simone Signoret. Chest x-ray by Ella Fitzgerald and then wheeled to the ward by Louis Armstrong and Fred Astaire. Admitted to the ward by Glenda Jackson, interned by Woody Allen, night orders written by Flora Robson. Tucked up in bed by Cleo Laine and given sedative by Tokyo Rose, Sibyl Thorndike, or Lena Horne (I forget which).

Digitalis and diuretics worked their usual miracles. Lost five kilograms in two days.

Four weeks later, while watching TV, there was a repeat performance. I was in a psychiatric hospital and was upset by a nurse applying petty rules in what I thought was a petty manner. Again I experienced a pain across the chest. It wasn't bad but it was accompanied by a sense of impending death. I was seen by the psychiatrist on duty who obviously thought that I was making an unnecessary fuss. I told him that I agreed that my condition was probably unimportant but recommended him to think of himself, just in case. I was transferred to the nearby, small community hospital where I was seen by the general internist on duty (Dustin Hoffman). He found some mild electrocardiographic changes and in the morning decided that I had better return to McMaster. It may sound as though he just passed the buck, but in fact, during that worrying night, he gave me the reassurance that he really was responsible in all the meanings of that word.

GENERAL CONCLUSIONS

Intensive care units vary in size and function. The typical ICU is usually described as a place where patients with disease of several body systems can be cared for by a team of nurses and doctors who provide the requisite range of skills. The ICU in the small hospital where I was on call is like that but the ICUs in the large hospital, where Diana was a patient, were really facilities for concentrated care of patients with disorders of a single body system. Fortunately communication was good – largely, I suspect, because of the quality of the surgeons and their long tradition of working together. The only glaring example of poor teamwork was in the care of her chest.

Responsibility is a big problem. I was impressed by the liaison between the orthopaedic surgeons, the neurosurgeons, and the general surgeons, as a result of which general surgery was at times quarterbacking Diana's care in an orthopaedic ICU. But again, this was due to the quality of the men not to the system.

Communication between these units and the relatives of the patients was almost non-existent. I do not think this is intentional; it simply reflects the ad hoc assumption of responsibility.

Ideally, I suppose, I would like to see the patient having one doctor who may "subcontract" to various specialists but without surrendering the overall care and who communicates with the relatives.

Of course the world is not ideal, but let's not give up.

A bloody bath

Although well settled in Hamilton, Ontario, Canada, "other things being equal" I would prefer to live in London, England and I think Diana feels the same. That preference is not to be construed as a criticism of Hamilton so much as an admission that I prefer London in respect of culture in the broadest sense. London inevitably has more to offer in terms of the arts but my idiosyncracies of taste, for example in sport – I prefer watching cricket to baseball and rugby and soccer to gridiron – also give London an edge. Furthermore as I enter old age the winter and its sports in Canada become less appealing as they do to many natives. It must be remembered also that I was forty three when I left London for Hamilton and so am more addicted to one than adaptable to the other. I have, therefore, been open to offers of jobs in Britain, in principle, but the catch lies in the qualification "other things being equal": three things have not been equal. Firstly I prefer the schools in Canada and, whether or not they are better, the children's education might be disrupted by a move. Secondly the jobs that have come my way are less challenging than the one I have done in Canada. Thirdly money is a problem. The first and third of these concerns are well and specifically illustrated by conditions a few years age. A professor in Britain was paid fifteen thousand pounds per annum. To send the children to Oxbridge would cost us (not having resided in the UK for the previous three years) five thousand pounds per annum per child. With three children at university, we obviously would have little left to live on.

I put these considerations to the dean at "St Swithin's" when he wrote and asked me if I would consider applying for the chair of medicine there. He subsequently phoned to say that he had the word of the chairman of the merit awards committee that I would have my income doubled within a year or so. The dean had also made some enquiries which suggested to him that if we played our cards right, particularly owning and living in our own home in London, our children would be eligible for grants to support university education. So, the arithmetic changed from income fifteen thousand pounds: education fifteen thousand pounds to income thirty thousand pounds: education five thousand pounds.

I agreed, therefore, to go and look at the job but I warned the dean that I did not want to get a bad name by turning it down on non-professional grounds that could have been identified beforehand. One Monday in September I flew to London (no sleep, hence jet lag to be anticipated) and set myself the task of attending to money, schooling, housing, etc in two or three days before appearing at St Swithin's.

I checked in at a good hotel whose switchboard I thought would be efficient, made a number of phone calls to try to arrange appointments for the next couple of days and tried, unsuccessfully, to get some sleep. The difficulty in making these phone calls immediately illustrated another way in which "other things" are not "equal". The people I had to deal with (phone operators, secretaries, and junior executives), although charming and seemingly helpful, are just not as concerned to solve one's problems as their opposite numbers are in North America. Thus I became thoroughly frustrated as the morning passed in unsuccessful attempts to arrange appointments and get information. No wonder I could not sleep. In the evening I gate crashed a cocktail party given by one of the private medico-scientific foundations to open an international symposium. And so to bed, but only managed two hours sleep.

Next morning I made more phone calls and then set off to see various people in the West End and City. I was uncomfortably high and got higher as I went from place to place and person to person. Sometimes the high was fuelled by getting some problem resolved. More often it was aggravated by the inability to get clear answers. I had originally intended to spend the evening with relatives or friends but decided I would be better advised to try to unwind at the theatre. So I took myself to the South Bank and saw one of the Shakespeare comedies done by the Young Vic (probably *Much Ado About a Tempest in a Midsummer Night's Dream*). And so to bed, but no sleep.

Next day more the same. Most of the memory is blurred but I remember the first "blood". My red pen had leaked into my shirt. When I grabbed a taxi to get from Regent's Park to St Paul's, I clutched my left breast and said to the driver, "Barts as quick as you can!" and took my hand away to reveal the red stain over my heart. As I settled in the cab, the driver slid back the partition and said, "Jees, Governor, you all right? Wouldn't it be better to go to Middlesex? it's closer."

"I'll be OK. They know about me at Barts. Just hurry up."

I then chatted with reasonable sangfroid and on reaching Barts gave the cabby a good tip, refusing his offer to help me into the hospital.

I had dinner by myself in Soho at one of Diana's and my favourite Italian restaurants and went to bed early. I slept soundly for three hours and awoke high but clear headed. I passed the rest of the night reading, writing letters, dictating notes into my portable tape recorder, and pacing the room.

Next morning I was ragged. I went to see the bank manager to try and clarify whether or not we would have to pay capital gains tax if we sold our house and moved closer to St Swithin's. Afterwards I had lunch in a pub near my old medical school, bought an instant camera, and began to play a game I shall call "providing evidence". This consisted of talking to a stranger and then taking two photographs – one of the person, which I kept, and one of myself, which I gave to him or her and asked them to keep in case they were ever asked about me!

Then I went into the medical school at which I had worked as a junior lecturer and looked up former colleagues and friends. If I found them I chatted wildly and took photographs. If I did not find them, I left bizarre manic messages.

In mid-afternoon I decided I must put myself in the hands of my good friends Elizabeth and John and took a taxi up to Hampstead, pausing en route to buy a case of Moet et Chandon. I found nobody at home so I emptied my pockets on the front porch and reinvented the match game. In this game one takes all the matches left in a box and arranges them on the ground to give the maximum amount of information. I think I found about twenty matches with which I managed to spell my initials, the time, and an arrow pointing to the Heath. I also wrote a short anagrammatic Joycean message on a scrap of paper and walked off to the Heath as far as the view over to Kenwood.

I sat there for half an hour or so before wandering back to E and J's. There I found Elizabeth very upset to have found all my possessions, including my passport and quite a lot of money, on the ground. She had not noticed the message in the arrangement of match sticks which, in her concern, she had just swept up. We talked and she cooled down. I babbled away and showed her how to write Joycean anagrammatic messages. We were later joined by husband John who did not understand my behaviour and was perturbed by it, and by daughter Emma who did understand and was not perturbed. We had dinner and they tried to persuade me to stay with them. I declined on the grounds that I was expecting several phone calls at the hotel and returned there about 11 pm and slept soundly.

I awoke thinking it must be 4 or 5 am and was surprised to find it was only 1 am. I needed a drink but had promised myself (and John) that I would keep off alcohol. I went downstairs and around the block. Nothing to be found. Noisy exchange with night porter who suggests that room service is best bet. For reasons which escape me I order two tomato joices, which take half an hour to come. Chastise the waiter and pointedly refuse to tip. He doesn't open bottles and I cannot find opener. Try to lever caps off using door hinges etc, but fail. In frustration try to break neck off bottle by hitting it on edge of lavatory bowl. Break both neck of bottle and lavatory bowl, spilling tomato joice in bowl. Unthinkingly, pull flush lever. Water swirls round neck of bowl spreading "blood"-stained water all over floor. Cut foot on broken glass. Go crazy. Sweating. Fill bath with tepid water, empty rest of tomato juice into it. Climb in and lie there trying to cool off while exploring the thought: "What if somebody were to see me like this?"

Knock on door. "This is the night manager Mr Campbell. Are you all right?"

"I am Professor Campbell. I am trying to sleep. Please go away."

A few minutes pause. "Professor Campbell, you have been making a disturbance. We are concerned about you. Please let me in"

After a few shouted remarks I climb out of the bath and open the bedroom door. A small excitable dark man pushes his way in and glances into the bathroom. "My Gott. What's going on?!", he exclaims in a thick Johannesburg accent. "Professor Campbell, I must insist that you leave the hotel immediately." I refuse and say I am just going to bed because I badly need sleep. He becomes very agitated and goes away. I try to sleep. No go, but feel quite peaceful. More knocks at the door. "It's the night manager again. Please let me in." "No." Muttered conversation outside door, which should have warned me. "If you don't, I will get the police."

Resignedly open the door and the manager bursts in, accompanied by a young constable. Then followed a lengthy disjointed conversation, the manager becoming increasingly agitated as he surveyed the mess in the bathroom and "blood" on the sheets. The policeman was soothing but kept giving the manager knowing looks. Eventually he got me to promise to stay in bed and took the manager away.

I lay there physically quiet but with my mind jumping around for what seemed like two hours. Then more knocking at the door and a woman's voice. "I am a nurse. Please let me have a look at you." Opened the door and in burst the manager, the policeman, and two women in civilian clothes, one of whom takes charge.

"Professor Campbell, we are psychiatric social workers. In

view of your behaviour and your state, we think you should come with us to hospital."

"For Christ's sake! All I need is some sleep. I'm not hurt and I can explain everything."

I try to, but they don't listen. Obviously, their minds are made up and I am unable to cope with a four way rapid fire conversation. I climb back into bed and pretend to sleep, but the psychiatric social workers keep talking at me: "It's for your own good. Come voluntarily or we'll have to use force." I refuse. After half an hour or so, the manager and the women withdraw, leaving the copper. I decide to call John and reach for the phone. The policeman prevents me. For the next hour or so I try to reason with him to let me call Diana or John. He refuses but I sense that I am gradually persuading him that I am not crazy when the manager and the social workers return with a bustling police inspector who tells me, in no uncertain manner, that I must go along with them.

"Where to?"

"That's up to you. Hospital if you behave: the station if you don't."

I feel rational contact with the world draining away. I even begin to feel frightened. To buy time, I ask to be allowed to dress, which I do slowly and deliberately. My mind is in too much turmoil to think out a rational plan. While they are off their guard, I rush out of the room and round the corner I find the fire escape door. For the next ten minutes I lead them a chase – which I quite enjoy as I repeatedly outguess them. Eventually I realise I cannot get away so I go back to my room and sit quietly waiting to be discovered. In some re-signed way I feel I am about to lose contact with the world as I know it, so I seize a flower vase by the neck. A strange new constable discovers me, enters the room, sees the vase in my hand, retreats to the corridor, and calls for help. Four men arrive and advance deliberately on me. I swing the vase at the mirror, shattering the glass and smash my watch on the wall.

"For God's sake, somebody remember that I only broke a mirror and that my watch stopped at 4.25 am."

My arms were pinned roughly behind me and I was hustled

downstairs to a vehicle which seemed more like an ambulance than a paddy wagon.

"Where are you taking me?"

"To hospital. You're lucky it isn't gaol."

Find the young policeman sitting beside me. "What the Devil is all this about? You know after the talk we had that I am not crazy – just tired out." He nods. "And why the Hell wouldn't you let me call my wife or best friend?"

"Just obeying orders."

On arrival at the hospital I am gently but firmly welcomed by a tall fair willowy night sister who puts me in a cubicle and sends a nurse to get Dr McLean.

Dr McLean came quite soon. He was an athletic looking young New Zealander – a senior, surgical house officer on call for the night. I told him my side of the story. He looked puzzled and went away. After a few more minutes, during which I surmised he phoned some senior person, he returned and told me without conviction that I must come into hospital.

"What if I refuse?"

"We will have to get an order from the DAO (Duly Authorised Officer) to commit you."

"Go ahead and try. I think I can persuade the DAO that I'm no danger to myself or anyone else."

"I don't think he'll believe you rather than the social workers after they describe your behaviour. And you would be better advised to have a few days rest here rather than in a psychiatric hospital."

The thought of losing "a few days" was too much. "Go ahead and get the DAO."

Dr McLean left and I was left more or less alone for what seemed an age. During this time I enjoyed myself telling Sister what had happened and how I would write a story, possibly even a movie, about the events of the last few days. I also tried to impress her by talking about the hospital indicating how well I knew many senior members of the staff. She seemed to listen but I think she was only humouring me.

Suddenly Dr McLean returned with two men whom I took to be male nurses. They and Sister held me while Dr McLean gave me an injection in the buttock. Again I felt the world I knew was rejecting me but after a brief struggle, during which I unthinkingly hit Sister quite hard, I went limp. I awoke in daylight in a bed in a large room with one other bed in it, occupied by a very tall and thin young man.

"Where am I?"

"We're in the...Hospital – the psychiatric ward." Pause. "In fact we're locked in the ward for 'disturbed patients'." As I later came to know, Ralph, my room mate, was no doubt disturbed. He was having marriage troubles. But there could hardly be a nicer, gentler person who needed locking up less.

About 7 am we were unlocked and accompanied through the hospital corridor to a good breakfast. Then I explored the limits to my new world. We were still locked in but now in the whole complex of rooms which constituted the ward rather than just in our own room. The centre of "life" was a large oblong room with chairs all round the walls, a tea urn, a television set, and a pay phone which we could use as much as we liked. I managed to accumulate about half a dozen 10 p coins and waited fretfully until 9 am. Then I began phoning and leaving messages to call back. That day I had to stay by the phone because there was no certainty that anybody answering it would know me or where to find me.

The feeling of being in something akin to a prison was intensified by the "medicine parade". We were summoned by a hand bell and stood in line while one nurse gave out the pills and another made sure we swallowed them. Several of the patients questioned their drugs and I later came to be sure there often were discrepancies between what the doctor told a patient he was to receive and what he in fact got, though whether this discrepancy was due to the doctor's failure to write the prescription or some other breakdown I did not establish. Psychiatric patients are very knowledgeable about their drugs and their side effects. The nurses were all firm but varied from being kindly, through being offhand, to downright brutal. I came to realise how the pressure of their work, the prison-like atmosphere, and the state of the patients had a brutalising effect on most of them, which, however, could be peeled away if one talked sensibly to them.

The day passed until the evening when I was very restless and begged to be allowed to go out for a walk. I was allowed out with a nurse but was told I must not leave the hospital grounds. I am ashamed to say that I gave her the slip and set off for Elizabeth and John's. After a few minutes I realised how futile it was to run away and went sheepishly back to the ward. I suffered by being locked in my room for the next twenty four hours and could only get out if accompanied by a nurse – and they were hard to come by. I was on large doses of drugs, particular the hated haloperidol, which made all movements clumsy and stiff, thereby making one look and feel more crazy than in fact one was.

I was visited by the consultant psychiatrist who listened sympathetically to my story and was obviously torn between his wish to help a "distinguished" colleague and his professional instinct. In retrospect I realise he took the risk of veering towrds the first of these inclinations. He lessened the restrictions on my movements, called Elizabeth, and encouraged her to come and go as often as she could, thus giving me a precious means of contact with the world other than the uncertain phone. He even allowed me out after three days but on the strict understanding that I would return to Canada as soon as possible and that Diana would immediately take me to another psychiatrist. I now realise how lucky I was in being in the care of that man.

John kindly arranged to take me to meet the dean of St Swithin's and four of his senior colleagues on the Sunday evening. There was no talk of my psychiatric troubles and to this day I do not know how widely my story was known; but I suspect the dean, at least, knew.

I told them that my enquires made me realise that there was no point in proceeding with interviews or negotiations because on general, non-professional grounds my explorations had convinced me that under present conditions I could not return to the UK. I gave them some advice about other candidates, based on my experiences in both London and McMaster, and we parted friends. They appointed an able, young chap I know quite well and he is doing fine.

And so, gratefully, back to the compassionate, cool, collected, calm companionship of Diana. I was quite well in a couple of days.

Highnights

It was of a night, late, lang time agone...when Adam was delvin and his madameen spinning. – JAMES JOYCE, *Finnegan's Wake*.

I was depressed from November 1981 until the following June. On the 26th and 27th of June I was particularly bad. I could only just get myself dressed and go to work and there I did nothing. I was struggling to prepare a lecture for a rather distinguished congress in Montreal but the ideas and words wouldn't come. I spent much of the day just pacing my office and went home early and dozed fitfully. About 10 pm on the 27th I felt sleep rushing over me, I just managed to get to bed before passing out. At 3 am I woke; the depression had lifted and I spent the rest of the night outlining the lecture, which came easily (and which I can soberly claim was, in the event, well received).

For the next few days I was worryingly high but coping. A week later we had a dinner party for eight at which I felt myself to be the life and soul of the party, although at times Diana was giving me signals to quieten down. The party broke up shortly before midnight and after we cleared up I fell deeply asleep until 2 am. Then I awoke suddenly full of energy and crept downstairs looking for something to do. It so happened that one of the guests, a delightful Scots visiting professor, had brought a nice little present: *A Taste of Scotland in Food and Pictures* by Theodora Fitzgibbon. It caught my eye and I turned over the pages, coming across such delicacies as Dundee cake, potato scones, broth, venison, porridge, bannocks, and hotch-potch. To pass the time, I annotated the recipes to indicate to Diana those which I particularly liked and how difficult they seemed (their "benefit:cost ratio"). Next I found myself making marginal notes of all sorts; the music I was listening to on the earphones, my earliest memory of having had these delicacies, memories of my parents. After an hour or two, the book was quite a mess and I feared Diana might think it spoiled.

For no memorable reason I placed the book on the coffee table and arranged a few objects to draw attention to it. Then I cast around for ways to indicate that my treatment of the book was loving, not desecratory. I had so written in the book but that was not enough for me and I found myself embarked on the preparation of a collage. To begin with most of the time was spent wandering slowly through the downstairs rooms picking up things which I felt had meaning for us and then arranging them. Later the balance of these activities tilted the other way; I sat quietly looking at the things on the table, occasionally moving them around.

I remember the following items which are listed approximately in the order in which I thought of them or found them. There were others but I have forgotten them. The cookbook; a single (artificial) red rose in a tall Swedish vase; a red, "phallengthy candle" in a silver candlestick; a modern, brass, Grecian statuette of Artemis; two, sexcited, soapstone seals; a brass, Turkish coffee grinder; a wine glass (initially clean but later half filled with Chateauneuf du Pape); an empty tin of Fry's cocoa; the LPs of *My Fair Lady* and Mozart's *Seventeenth Piano Concerto* ("Madagain"); a coffee table book on the Impressionists; my own first, slim book in its pink and black dusty jacket; *Popper* by Magee (with a book marker at page eighty five); an empty ball point and a broken pencil; a burnt out light bulb; my passport; a packet of Rothmans (wish it had been Woodbines); an empty bottle of Valium with a few tablets scattered about; a Swiss army knife with both corkscrew and blade extended.

When most of these things had been collected and as I was pondering the arrangement, I decided I needed a striking armorican background. So I crept up to the bedroom and groped in her drawer until I found a much known Macy lacy shortie. And in passing I took a bottle of *Je Reviens*. Then I went back down to the sitting room, took everything off the table, and laid the nightie on it, sprinkled with *Here I come Again* (in French). For the next hour or so I peacefully explored various arrangements seeking to "maximise the information content" ("wringing the most massage out of the media").

The final arrangement was probably indescribable. Anyway I only remember the centrepiece: the candle in its stick standing on the Scots cookbook which had started me off; this book in turn resting on the wine glass. (Sounds unstable but on testing it resisted quite strong shocks.) In general each of the things I used has a superficial meaning of symbolism, so obvious as to be corny, but to me (and I hoped to Diana) each specific example spoke peculiarly to our memories – even the cocoa tin.

All the while I was feeling my inability to communicate with Diana in words. We do well in other ways. I was afraid that she would take my behaviour at the party and the evidence of how I had spent the night as signs that things were getting out of hand. I went upstairs and lay down for a short while but my body and mind were jumping all over the place when the idea occurred to make this problem a vehicle with which to try and convey the relief I get from "Joycean" writing. I would write passages in plain English and in Joycean in such a way that people who took the trouble could see how quickly Joyspeak can be written. The diary of that exercise forms the rest of this chapter. It has been subjected to the minimum editing required for printing. When high I can write at twice the speed in Joyspeak but more important than speed is the pleasure I get from the juxtaplay of syllables or even single letters in hinting at meanings other than the simple message.

Few will be surprised that I call this writing Joycean or Joyspeak, although Anthony Burgess has pointed out its progenitor in the portmanteau wordings of Humpty Dumpty. It can of course be dismissed as punning; but is punning to be regarded as merely trivial?

Let me attempt to impose some system on the game, recognising that a rigid categorisation is impossible (and that my effort will risk punity – ugh!)

I recognise four grades of increasing complexity.

Firstly the swapping of letters or words leaving spelling, grammar, and syntax (almost) normal. These are the stuff of the common pun and Spoonerism (Madam! Your ship is slowing; a well-boiled icycle; where the bus stops there shop I; I have satisfactory relations with my charted accuntant).

Secondly the foreign letter or syllable in a word which multiplies its meaning(s), grammar and syntax still normal (Armorica, sinduced, slithy, usquilateral – these are typical portmanteau words; even the simplest of them – "slithy" – embreeds foursum.)

Thirdly a sentence using neologisms but still observing the rules of grammar and syntax. This is the Joyspeak typical of *Ulysses*, but my first examples come from *Finnegan's Wake* (Sir Tristram, violer d'amores, fr'over the short sea, had passencore rearrived…to wielderfight his penisolate war; our cubehouse still rocks as earwitness to the thunder of his arafatas).

Fourthly a cluster of syllables which leave the reader to savour the hints of meanings. There is no overt grammar or syntax. inoyincreaseyornitendalife/ndwelintoyrsexnhows-wife – here the metre helps to get you started but in the long run it is a hindrance – bababadalgharaghtakammin-arronnkonnbronntonnerronntuonnthunntrovarrhounawns kawntoohoohoordenenthurnuk (the most notorious of Joyce's concoctions).

Many of the examples above are taken from *Finnegan's Wake*. They are to be savoured for their hints rather than merely scanned for their meaning. To be transarty: Picassulook! Obviously there is a limit to what the reader can take. (Sometimes, but not very often, I find pieces I myself have written some time ago difficult to understand.) I suspect that Joyce strayed beyond the limit in *Finnegan's Wake* and lost many readers who could cope with *Ulysses*.

I would be presumptuous to wrightin the same bearth of my tryvia and the masterpeace of *Finnegan's Wake* which took seventeen Joyceful years of work to progress but I surpraise myself as letters and ideas feel and feed and fight and foil each other in reeling time like now and then.

DIARY

And now for my diary of the early hours of 4 July. First in approximately standard English. Written, I emphasise, in real time, very legibly in lower case.

4.30 am. Lay in bed in spare room. Peaceful. Tired but not sleepy, limbs quiet; no need to turn over. Soft euthermic sweat.

4.38 am. Preoccupied with what to do about the cookbook and the collage. Afraid Diana will be upset by both but I must let her see them – but not have me explain them.

 I would like Black (Peter the shrink) to see the book but only if Di agrees and blue pencils offences against her person.
4.50 am. Raining (not supposed to). My bird sings. Must identify the churp chap. Go out in my dressing gown. Wet. Little light so no sight.
4.55 am. Want a smoke but fags buried in collage. Remember cigars in desk. No light; use cooker.
4.59 am. Nauseated, even pukewary. Shouldn't inhale cigar.
4.59–5.06 am. Pause. Contemplate and fine-tune the collage. And sip a little Chateau NDP

NOW IN JOYSPEAK

Written again in real time but in firm clear capitals, using varied emphasis and spacing which is difficult to reproduce.

5.06. LAYQUITECOOLDAMPREST NOGITATION NODEEPRESSURINGS. WRIGTESLOW TO SHOW NOT JESTSPEED/TRIK. WHATODOBOUTHEODORA-BLOOK?
5.07. ?MUSTELDIANPETEBOUTLOASTHRS HOPE-THINK (THINKHOPE?) PETE IS JOYCEMAN SADIANA-INT (DINAMITE CHAN/RGE – ugh!) COLLARGER THAN DILIKE BUT DONT WANTWO DECOLLAGE

231

(Ugh!) BFORSHOWPETABOOKNEEDIANAHELP –
FI(R)STASENSOR...
5.09. 2 MINOPAUSE COS ZGARGONOUT.
DIFFUCKALTRYFINDELITE.
5.11. ZEDGARGOINGAIN BACGTRYINFIN<u>DI</u>LOVER-
SLEAPIN(H)OURS. (PS WHENUBUSEAWORD PLAY-
ITXTRA – TAHUMPTY)

TRANSCRIPTION

Still in real time. What follows is copied from what I wrote
at the time; the manuscript is clear and only a dozen minor
corrections were needed.

5.45. Now let me try and write clearly. What was going
through my mind and on to the paper in the two periods
4.30–4.59 am and 5.06–5.45 am.

How and when shall I tell Diana what I have done to her
Scottish cookery book? I must decide first on some principles.
Do I tell her at all or simply put the book away until the
present high, which is probably worrying her, has settled
down? So far I had not considered any alternative. However,
I think I should show it to my shrink whatever Diana may
think of my ramblings and ravings. In the longer run, I would
like to have her help because; if they can be explained to her,
she may be less worried and she may even be pleased –
perhaps (DV) amused – by the collage and by my scribblings.
And with better understanding and less worry she may be less
opressive to me. There are three possible courses of action.

Firstly tell her when I take her a morning cup of tea before
breakfast. Not a good idea because she is liable to be upset
too soon; she is not at her best in the morning.

Secondly don't say anything about the book at first but
show her the collage. Not a good idea because she will be
upset by the collage and will only glance through the book
and see it as evidence of my mania and miss the love I have
tried to convey – and the good humour. She may even be so

upset by the apparent mess I have made of the book that she will throw it away or tear it up.

Thirdly wait until she is up and about when she is her usual equable self and hope that she is intrigued and amused by the collage before she finds the book. There is no real hurry – I can wait until Sunday evening.

I finished writing just after 6.30 am and made myself a large mug of café au diable. While sipping it I made minor adjustments to the collage. Then I lit the candle (not easily done) and cycled off to the lab. A glorious morning.

I freely admit that to the uninvolved reader the substance of this episode seems trivial but it was not trivial to me: I was worried that I would not be understood by Diana who would add the evidence of my behaviour last night to the other evidence that I was again becoming "psychotically" manic.

In the event, after cycling into my office, I worked on my Montreal lecture (I had left a note on the breakfast table to that effect). Robert, our son, was first to come downstairs in the morning. He found the collage, decided that it would worry Mother and was clear evidence that I was in trouble and, in any case, was a fire hazard. He dismantled the collage and phoned me virtually ordering me either to come home or call Peter.

I finished my work and went home to find Robert very upset and aggressive and Diana insistent on calling Peter. Robert refused to give me the book which I think he said would at best be worrying to Mother and at worst would be offensive to her. It turned up some weeks later. Diana understands what I did to it but doesn't like it.

Three days later my behaviour had so upset most of the folks at home and work that I had to be put away. I went voluntarily because I wanted to get away from people. I should, however, have remembered the bloody bath. I had again to submit to the cold hell of alienation in a "well run" hospital with its rules and "privileges" (Orwellangod) designed for the benefit of the administrators, doctors, nurses, other patients, and me in that order of priority. And the dread haloperidol which reduces me to a shuffling zombie unable to write and scarcely able to speak.

It so happened that among the books I had brought with me was the *Fontana Dictionary of Modern Thought*. I find it instructive and entertaining even when my span of attention is down to a few seconds. Browsing through the twenty two "antis" I came across the following entry by Hope Liebersohn:

Anti-psychiatry. A movement in therapeutic practice, initiated by RD Laing and others, which rejects conventional PSYCHIATRY and regards the CONCEPT of mental illness as both unscientific and stigmatizing; mental illness may, indeed, be a healthy response to a sick society. Psychiatrists and mental hospitals are regarded as agents of social repression, in league with the family and with society at large in putting pressure on non-conforming individuals; and certain procedures of psychiatry, eg LEUCOTOMY, ELECTRO-CONVULSIVE THERAPY, and tranquillizing drugs, as well as any authoritarian PSYCHOTHERAPY, are seen as obstructing the proper, self-directed resolution of personality disorders.

Moranagreamotrulikenastiness.

PS Typescript finally corrected while listening, à la Lew, the peeping Thom, to Mahler's Ninth. Kreatsquip in album note: "half in love with easeful death". The state, yes; the process, how?

On being manic depressive

Dr Noel Harris gleamed from his brylcreemed hair to the tips of his patent leather shoes. In between these extremes his slender figure carried the Harley Street uniform of the 'thirties; carbon dark grey jacket and grey striped trousers. His tie was silvery but understated. To the students of the fourth year he gave three lectures, one on personality types, one on the neuroses, and one on the psychoses. These lectures were supplemented by a visit to the lunatic asylum at Shenley where were shown patients with classic psychoses; schizophrenia, mania and depression, and one with extreme, compulsive, obsessional neurosis who would spend half an hour washing her hands if she touched anything that "felt dirty". That was the extent of the curricular treatment of psychiatry. We were welcome to attend the psychiatry clinic which myself and two or three other students did in the hope of seeing people as entertaining as the hallucinated schizophrenic who had talked to non-existent relatives at Shenley. But the stock in trade at the clinic was rather dull: miserable housewives and spotty bed wetters. We gave up on psychiatry, therefore, until finals approached when we boned up on the classic stigmata of schizophrenia and the affective disorders.

At the start of his first lecture Dr Harris bounced to the blackboard and wrote in large and well spaced capital letters.

1 NEUROTIC
2 SCHIZOID PARANOID
3 CYCLOTHYMIC or MANIC DEPRESSIVE
4 HYSTERICAL

These he told us were the personality types and then he described them while we silently diagnosed ourselves and our colleagues. Punctually, on the hour, Dr Harris fastidiously brushed the chalk from his hands and strode to the door. By tradition we clapped – he was the only lecturer we applauded. At the door he turned with a knowing smile and bowed elegantly from the waist. Ham and I walked round the corner to get a cup of tea at the local Joe Lyons. Hamilton was a mature student who had been injured in the leg early in the war, so we walked slowly while Ham drew on his pipe. We were silent until seated in the cafe.

"Well that put us in our slots; you a schizoid and me a neurotic", I offered.

Ham both nodded and shook his head. "Nonsense. I'm schizoid all right but you're not neurotic, you're manic depressive."

That was the first hint and for twenty five years it was the only one. At times I was depressed and at times I was unduly happy, particularly when working hard. By and large I thought I was normal and the association of insomniac happiness with hard work I took as evidence of obsessionalism. The truth was revealed by my second visit to Hamilton (*So This is Hamilton-McMaster*).

Since then, for eighteen years, coping with it has dominated my life. For the first eight years I think I coped pretty well. I ran on a roughly weekly cycle: low on Sunday/Monday and high on Thursday/Friday. For the last seven years, however, I have been mostly depressed: a sort of existence between short bursts of hypomania. On three occasions I have been pathologically manic and have had to "go away". I have already described the first of these: now I will describe what I feel and do when very depressed and very manic.

For a start, at this instant it is 5.35 am and I have been writing for two hours because it is more relaxing than lying or rather tossing in bed while my mind jumps around. For the first hour I had The Duke on the headphones. Since daybreak I have been serenaded by a lone catbird. Now I am going to make a mug of café au diable (laced with a jigger of rye). I will sip it, smoke a pipe, listen to Mozart, and think how to spend the next three hours.

SAME TIME, TWO DAYS LATER

I spent the next hour pottering about in the basement tidying up the wine making. I rearranged my stock of empty bottles and regrouped the full bottles on the rack to make room for the ten gallons (fifty bottles) which were waiting to be bottled. Then I went off on the ten-speed, up the mountain and turned east along the mountain brow with no particular route in mind. A gorgeous morn. Red sun over misty mirror lake. Gardens at their best. Loudly "good morning" all the joggers. How miserable half of them look. Rhythmically locked to the bike, pumping along at twenty. Zen and the Art of Pedal Pushing.

After ten miles or so I decided to breakfast at Susie's (daughter number two—my Tiffany). So after fifteen miles, I turned down the mountain on the New Mountain Road. I must have topped forty mph on the descent (really should wear a crash helmet – suggest to Susie that it would make a good birthday present). It's July 1st, the Dominion Day holiday, so I mustn't arrive at Susie's too soon. Set myself an ETA of 8.30 am and use up the last ten minutes zigzagging the streets near her home. Susie opens the door, deliciously sleepy, still pulling on the black and white yukata we bought her in Tokyo. She is very matter of fact, tells me that husband Alan has gone off to race his motorcycle and says, "'spose you've come for breakfast." The next ninety minutes pass in good chat with Susie and so back home to wake Diana. I have passed the night.

July 1 passes easily doing inconsequential things like playing tennis, watching the World Cup and Wimbledon, reading a few pages of a few books, bottling wine, and being with Diana. I pass out abruptly at 10.30 pm and come round at 1.30 am. I Joycewrite much of the night but the day is troublesome. Bags of energy but too exhausted and lacking in concentration to do anything, even lying down for more than ten minutes. Keep losing things. Ten pm take two pills, pass out at 11.00 pm, and sleep until 5.30 am. Today is going to be grreatefull.

ACTIVITIES OF DAILY LIVING

Waking ends the night and begins the day. When I am well, I wake with the radio at 7.15 am. Sometimes it is first but usually I beat it by ten or fifteen minutes. When I am either too up or too down, however, I usually beat it by two or three hours. When really high, I wake at 2 or 3 am.

What to do when wakening at 3 am? The first thing to do is to feel, and that is not always easy. On occasion it takes several seconds to discover who I am and a few more to determine where I am; then, and only then, does the feeling that anticipates those realisations come into focus. But focus is not really the right word – "context" is more apposite. Does what I am feeling make sense? Not easy to decide, particularly as one passes through a dream on the way to the surface of consciousness. Ironically, when down, the net result is agreeable on two counts. Firstly, "Thank God I don't have to face the world for another few hours". Secondly the non-specific feeling – the miasma of depression – does not seep into me until 7 am or thereabouts. On the other hand, early wakening when high is a sign that I am going to have diffiulty putting my thoughts together and getting through the day without disgracing myself. My fuse is too short for other people's comfort or my own good.

Whether high or low, there is a discrepancy between thought, feeling, and energy. If down, I cannot find a reason or the energy to do anything, even if I happen to find remediable problems. If high, I cannot find sensible things to do to channel the energy. If down, I try to think of reasons to get out of bed; if high, I try to fill my mind with "white thought" (the cerebral equivalent of "white noise") in the hope of getting back to sleep. The best known white thought is sheep counting but it is too boring to sustain so I play "people and places". I start in London and let someone in London come into my mind and then I connect him or her with another place (often the connections are very tenuous – they have to be made very quickly to prevent a train of thought) and so to another person. White thought can also help depressive in-somnia but it is not as effective and in any case one usually wallows back into a twilit, time passage that decimates the hours.

Whichever the mood, the enemy is time. If depressed, the problem is to pass it with a semblance of purpose until I can next hold sleep's hand and pass out. If manic, the problem is how to spin out the things I want to do to occupy the time that normal people allot to them. As the shrinks say, I am troubled by "flights of ideas" and "press of activities". The distortion of the sense of time surprises most people, including many psychiatrists. Intuitively they feel that time must lie heavy when depressed and that there isn't enough time when manic: but I find the reverse to be true. When depressed, hours can pass unnoticed before an unread book or an unseen TV. When manic, even minutes expand until it seems impossible to fill them: I rush about not because time is short but because it is so long that I find it difficult to fill.

The practical world asserts itself on rising: how to washave and howhat to wear? A shower is invigorating but the initial shock of the water is an obstacle. A proper shave is invigorating but the soaping and scraping are obstacles, so I shower and shave when high and use an electric razor and forego the shower when low. When high, I take a modicum of pleasure in deciding what to wear. When low, I have to choose my clothes the night before or I will wear the same for days on end. The next problem is breakfast. If high, I like to prepare something and take it to Diana in bed. If low, I can only manage a bowl of cereal and a cup of tea, and if they are not awaiting me I may forego anything.

Next problem: how to get to work? If high, there is no problem; I bicycle winter and summer. If low, I can think of innumerable excuses for going by car.

When either too low or too high, I have trouble with concentration and memory but in different ways. When low, I just cannot dig up the details from my memory. When high, I can concentrate intensely but only for a few seconds and my memory is interrupted by changes of thought. The telephone is a good example of the difference. When really low, I have difficulty with familiar numbers; when really high, I cannot remember new ones. They leave my mind as soon as I find them in the directory; I have to keep them in sight as I dial. In extremis I may forget who I am calling. Yet when moderately high I can formulate ideas and analyse problems with a speed and precision that I can never match when "normal".

When high, I am afraid of relatives, minor officials, and friends but not of strangers. When low, I don't like to meet any of them but they do not frighten me.

To those who have never been really depressed it is probably easier to understand the sadness, the greyness, the hopelessness, and the thoughts of suicide than to sympathise with the lack of energy or drive, the overwhelming inertia. To me, however, the lack of energy is the bigger problem and I cannot over-emphasise this dissociation between the mood of depression and the lassitude of depression. I can reason intellectually about the sad things and see that I am unreasonable but I cannot do anything about the inertia. There is a limit to the extent to which one can "pull oneself together" when even washing and dressing become major tasks. Even if I can make the effort I do whatever I do slowly and badly. There are, however, discrepancies in that generalisation. When I am depressed I may have difficulty in changing my clothes but I can still function quite well in such demanding activities as lecturing. This paradox hinges on the need for initiative in the one activity and not in the other. I have a contract to give the lecture and the programme for it – getting there, arranging the slides, etc – takes over. Any initiative would have to be to arrange not to give the lecture and taking that step would be even more distressing. On the other hand, I have no contract to change my clothes. Most of life's activities are closer to changing clothes than to lecturing so the difficulties of coping with these activities are very pervasive. I have evolved a way of coping which goes through three stages: countermanding, contracting, and programming. I will continue with the example of clothes changing. The idea that I should change my clothes is unwelcome but particularly as it usually arises in the morning when I am at my lowest. Within a split second of the appearance of the idea, I will try to suppress it with some rationalisation such as "my blue trousers need cleaning", "my black shoes are uncomfortable", or whatever. I must immediately countermand this response and make a contract to change my clothes, not now, not just later, but tonight. As night approaches I will work out a programme to deal with the selection, preparation, and arrangement of the garments so that tomorrow morning I have no decisions to make.

I realise that all normal people are from time to time "bugged" by not wanting to be bothered with such trivia as changing their clothes. Agreed. The difficulty I find when depressed is quantitative, not qualitative. It is like walking through soft sand or deep snow. I get slower and slower and just want to lie down; but then doing nothing rouses the angst. An ironical consequence of this lack of energy is that I do things long before they need to be done because of my fear that, if I wait, I will not be able to do them at all. Let it not be thought, however, that I am just recounting the common experiences of tiredness or fatigue. I may be desperately tired when manic but rarely when depressed.

Ironically, the inertia of depression makes killing myself very difficult because I just cannot think of a way to kill myself painlessly without making a mess of my body and without distressing the family. The risk I fear is suddenly being faced with the opportunity to kill myself on the spur of the moment. Of course if I really put my mind to it I could devise a means. The fact that I don't is, I suppose, a sign that I never really despair. I do have a pact with myself, however, that even when I have the energy I will never stockpile arms or pills for use in the event.

Not that I haven't made gestures. I have looked over precipices, tasted cyanide, toyed with a bare bodkin, and dared myself to crash the bicycle or car. I just cannot be bothered. Passive suicide thoughts are much easier. Thus I was quite at ease, almost enthusiastic, when I had a heart attack which threatened my life and was tranquil when stacked and buffeted over New York in a winter storm for an hour. No effort was demanded of me and my end would bring sympathy to the family and not disgrace.

I could go on. The pending tray is empty when high, full

when low; I want good weather so I can sail, ski, cycle, or play tennis when high. I welcome rain and bad weather forecasts when low. I welcome committee meetings when low: I destroy them when high. I love shopping when high: I cannot be bothered to buy my lunch when low. When high, I catch the plane before the one I have booked and flush the loo when only half finished.

The physical symptoms match the psychological. I am cold and still when low; hot, shaky, and sweaty when high. In neither state can I write; my hand cannot be dragged across the paper when low; my writing is illegible when high. I am not sure whether weeping is psychological or physical. In any event, it is troublesome in the present century. And it is paradoxical: I weep when high, never when low. Thus I have had tears streaming down my face at – admittedly a very good – production of *The Tempest* or the final scene of *My Fair Lady*. By contrast, even *The Trojan Woman* cannot engage me emotionally when low.

Overall there is the vicious paradox: I like myself when high but other people find it much easier to take me when I am low. Indeed my family and colleagues dread my highs which, in truth, can be very hurtful and very damaging. To this generalisation I think I must make one exception. I cannot of course speak for my wife's feelings but my own are a mix on which I think I can rely: my feeling for her, my feeling of hers for me, and my feeling of her feeling of my feeling for her. I am persuaded that she is anguished by the unsmiling misery she lives with and which I do not trouble to hide. How does she maintain an appearance of normality? Thank God she does.

The swings, although infrequent, are very sudden. The cloud of depression can grip me in an hour or so and mania can make me impossible in a couple of days. (My recognition of its onset takes much less time.) What triggers the switches? The only regular precipitating factor is jet lag. On at least three occasions, jet lag has been followed by a high. I cannot identify anything comparable that throws the other switch but the profound depression that assailed me when I gave up the excitement of being chairman of the department of medicine was so clearly post hoc as to suggest that it was also propter hoc. Colleagues too have recounted the same experience.

MANAGEMENT

Managing both the highs and the lows has been chiefly my business but I have had great help from Diana and the family and also from several psychiatrists.

The key to my own efforts has been "avoiding action". When high, I have to minimise my contact with other people both because it excites me and also because what I say and how I behave may lack good judgement. If I can get enough sleep, good undrugged sleep, I can cope. I can go for weeks on four to six hours but am in bad trouble if I have a couple of nights with less than two hours.

Of course it is not possible to avoid all contact, so I often find myself becoming aggressive, talking too much, and interrupting the people I am talking to. It is not always easy just to stop and walk away. A psychiatrist wisely suggested I observe a "five minute" rule. He told me to spot trouble five minutes ahead, decide then to leave, and use the five minutes to develop some face-saving strategy to get out of the situation.

When depressed, I have to avoid making commitments that are beyond my mental means. It is all very well to say that I will give a lecture or write something at some distance in the future. No matter how much time I have, I must not attempt tasks beyond my resources because the angst I suffer just makes things worse. This avoidance is not easy because the shame that goes with it, although less, is nevertheless a problem in its own right.

Psychiatrists have been very helpful, not because of the drugs they have given me, for these have not worked, but because I can talk to them. Their role is to listen. I do not have to please them. This ability or right to talk freely is welcome, particularly when depressed. I do not find it easy to talk freely with many relatives or friends because I do not want to bother them and they want to help; our roles are to please each other.

Three years ago while hypomanic, I fell asleep when driving. The accident has left Diana with some nerve damage in the legs which impairs her ability to play tennis and ski and takes away much of the pleasure of life. Since that time, I have also been persistently, but probably coincidentally, depressed. We support each other but it is difficult to find the energy other than for existence. We should both improve. In her case the improvement will unfortunately be slow. In my case it is to be hoped that improvement will be slow. A sudden high spell, though delightful, would be bad news.

On one matter my mind has been changed; the way I wish to die. Until a few years ago I subscribed to the common desideratum: to drop dead from a heart attack. Now I would like a bit more, not agony or the long drawn out misery of my father's going, but I would like to be allowed time to think about it, write about it, and perhaps talk about it (if people will permit me to). And some pain might be in order, enough to compare with the "psychic pain" of depression.

But of course I expect to feel differently when the time comes.

References

WHAT IS PHYSIOLOGY

Campbell EJM. An electromyographic study of the role of the abdominal muscles in breathing. *J Physiol* 1952; **117**: 222–33.
Bowers E, Campbell EJM, Johnston CHP. Factors promoting venous return from the arm in man. *Lancet* 1945; i: 460–1.
Campbell EJM. *The respiratory muscles and the mechanics of breathing.* London: Lloyd-Luke, 1958.

BLOODY GASES

Riley RL, Campbell EJM, Shepard RH. A bubble method for estimation of PCO_2 and PO_2 in whole blood. *J Appl Physiol* 1957: **11**: 245–9.
Campbell EJM, Martin HB, Riley RL. Mechanisms of airway obstruction. *Bull Johns Hopkins Hosp* 1957; **101**: 329–43.
Shepard RH, Campbell EJM, Martin HB, Enns T. Factors affecting the pulmonary dead space as determined by single breath analysis. *J Appl Physiol* 1957; **11**: 241–4.

RESPIRATORY FAILURE IN THE 'FIFTIES

Campbell EJM. Respiratory failure 30 years ago. *Br Med J* 1979; **2**: 657–8.
Westlake EK, Campbell EJM. Effects of aminophylline, nikethamide, and sodium salicylate in respiratory failure. *Br Med J* 1959; i: 274–6.

CONTROLLING OXYGEN

Campbell EJM. Respiratory failure. The relation between oxygen concentrations of inspired air and arterial blood. *Lancet* 1960; ii: 10–11.
Campbell EJM. A method of controlled oxygen administration which reduces the risk of carbon-dioxide retention. *Lancet* 1960; ii: 12–14.
Campbell EJM. The J. Burns Amberson Lecture: The management of acute respiratory failure in chronic bronchitis and emphysema. *Am Rev Resp Dis* 1967; **5**: 626–39.

DADDY SAYS DO A Pco_2

Campbell EJM and Howell JBL. Simple rapid methods of estimating arterial and mixed venous pCO_2. *Br Med J* 1960; i: 458–62.

Campbell EJM. Simplification of Haldane's apparatus for measuring CO_2 concentration in respired gases in clinical practice. *Br Med J* 1960; i: 457–8.

"A BEING BREATHING THOUGHTFUL BREATHS"

Campbell EJM, Freedman S, Smith PS, Taylor ME. The ability of man to detect added elastic loads to breathing. *Clin Sci* 1961; 20: 223–31.

Bennett ED, Jayson MIV, Rubenstein D, Campbell EJM. The ability of man to detect added non-elastic loads to breathing. *Clin Sci* 1962; 23: 155–62.

Campbell EJM, Howell JB. The sensation of breathlessness. *Br Med Bull* 1963; 19: 36–40.

Campbell EJM, Howell JB. Proprioceptive control of breathing. In: deReuck AVS, O'Connor M, eds. *Ciba foundation symposium on pulmonary structure and function.* London: Churchill, 1962: 29–45.

Howell JB, Campbell EJM. *Breathlessness. Proceedings of an international symposium held on April 7, 8, 1965 under the auspices of the University of Manchester.* Oxford: Blackwell Scientific Publications, 1966.

"BREATH'S A WARE THAT WILL NOT KEEP"

Campbell EJM, Freedman S, Clark TJH, Robson JG, Jones NL. The effect of muscular paralysis induced by tubocurarine on the duration and sensation of breath-holding. *Clin Sci* 1967; 32: 425–32.

Campbell EJM, Godfrey S, Clark TJH, Freedman S, Norman J. The effect of muscular paralysis induced by tubocurarine on the duration and sensation of breath-holding during hypercapnia. *Clin Sci* 1969; 36: 323–8.

SO THIS IS HAMILTON–McMASTER

Campbell EJM. The McMaster Medical School at Hamilton, Ontario. *Lancet* 1970; ii: 763–7.